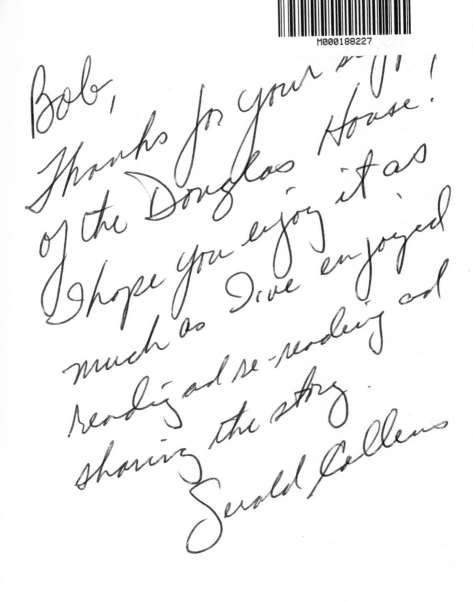

Bob,
Thanks for your ___ !
of the Douglas House!
I hope you enjoy it as
much as I've enjoyed
reading and re-reading and
sharing the story.
Gerald Collins

Douglas House

The Adventures of an African-American
Sailor In London During the Vietnam War

Gerald A. Collins

1st WORLD
LIBRARY
The World's Publisher

Austin, Texas

Douglas House
©Gerald A. Collins, 2004

1st World Library
7600 Burnet Road, Suite 510
Austin, TX 78757
512-339-4000
www.1stworldlibrary.com

Library of Congress Control Number: 2004090486
ISBN: 0-9745624-0-8

First Edition

Senior Editor
Barbara Foley

Editors
Carolyn Toye
Brad Fregger
Bob Mahoney

Book and Cover Design
Amelia Nottingham-Martin

Cover Photograph by Amelia Nottingham-Martin

I dedicate this book to my mother, Grace Smallwood Collins. May she rest in peace. She inspired me to dream big dreams. I love her and miss her immeasurably.

I also dedicate it to my children in the hope that telling my story will inspire them to share their stories, because we, as a people, and as a nation, have gone too long not knowing each other's stories.

Acknowledgements

I am grateful to all those who overlooked my long absence and assisted me in finally telling *our* story. I am particularly grateful to my wife Margaret for allowing me the freedom to explore memories and reopen doors that were crucial to the creation of this work.

I am grateful to the people of St. Thomas Episcopal Church, Red Bank, New Jersey, for their consideration and understanding of my work and my past, particularly as it relates to their church, their community, and in particular, one family.

I am especially grateful to the men and women who lived the story of *Douglas House*. Our joint experiences helped lay the foundation for my ongoing quest to learn more about myself and to find meaning in the crisscrossing paths that lead, inevitably, back to my God.

I would be remiss if I did not thank Carolyn Toye, my editor, for her enduring patience in turning my writings into this story of *Douglas House.*

Finally, I would like to thank the good folks at 1st World Library, especially Brad Fregger, for their encouragement and their much-appreciated efforts in turning my story into this book.

Preface

Douglas House is my coming-of-age story as a young man in mid-sixties London told through my fictional alter ego, Harry Butler. Many times over the past three decades, I have started writing the story of *Douglas House*. No matter how hard I tried, I could not complete it. However, in the past ten years, a series of events have occurred that culminated in an emotional outpouring that literally thrust the story into being.

In 1991, I joined the American Red Cross as a disaster liaison working with communities and churches (often poor and minority churches) throughout the United States, focusing on disaster preparedness and response. Since 1999, I have been the Director of Disaster Response for Catholic Charities USA.

The events of September 11, 2001, resulted in the loss of thousands of lives. And while the greatest loss of life occurred in New York City at the World Trade

Center, and in Washington, DC at the Pentagon, more than 250 people who lost their lives that day lived within the Roman Catholic Diocese of Trenton, New Jersey. Of that number, more than 100 people lived in Monmouth County, home to Neptune and Red Bank, New Jersey. I spent a great deal of time in these two towns from 1965 to 1968, time that played an important role in molding me into the man I am today.

After the September 11 attacks, I felt a tug from the old Neptune and Red Bank of my youth asking me to help. Then in April 2002, quite by chance, my work with Catholic Charities brought me to Neptune. I am now bringing my experiences of the past ten years, and the resources of my office, to the Monmouth County community by helping them to create a more effective community disaster preparedness, response, and recovery network.

I am in awe of the circumstances that returned me to a community that has meant so much to me. I feel humbled that God provided me this opportunity to assist them as they continue to recover from the events of September 11. Sadly and ironically, those events and subsequent activities re-ignited my passion, finally enabling me to tell the story of *Douglas House.*

CHAPTER ONE

Enlisting

The sixties were years of tremendous upheaval in America. Students demonstrated on college campuses; government and civic leaders were assassinated; troops with fixed unsheathed bayonets patrolled the streets; and our cities were ablaze with the anger and frustration of a generation coming of age. Most of that anger and frustration was focused on the undeclared war that raged in Vietnam.

For young black men, the war was particularly onerous because we were dying in numbers disproportionate to the general population. We were intimately involved in the conflict, as we humped the Long-Range Recon Patrols in places with exotic names such as Ben Hoi, Ke Sahn, My Lai, and the Qua Trang Valley. We were the grunts in the foxholes. We were the medics tending the wounded and surrounded by death. We died when we stepped on land mines, were shot by snipers, or were victims of friendly fire. Our families mourned us as our bodies came home in sealed caskets. But some of us were fortunate and escaped to a safer place.

In the spring of 1965, I longed to be rid of what I called my in-between years, the time between eighteen and twenty when you are no longer a teenager and too young to be legally considered an adult. In the two-plus years since high school graduation I had, in my opinion, become a man. I had left home, had my own apartment, and was paying $99 per month rent, plus utilities. I had a full-time *good* job, as the old folks would say; I was a GS-5 working in a highly-sought-after intelligence agency making in excess of $5000 per year. And to top it off, I was a college student, albeit part-time. In the words of that day, *I was making it.*

To let the world know I was making it, I had affected the air of a man of accomplishment. I wore suits as often as I could afford; I drank Cuba Libres instead of plain old rum and cokes or beer; and on my planned outings, I took bus trips to Baltimore and, occasionally, New York. In my mind, I was a man of the world.

As spring turned to summer, I had three things on my mind: the Vietnam War, the draft, and a young lady named Rachel Morrissey. However, Rachel Morrissey was the most stable and least worrisome element of the trio. I had no idea that all three elements would soon converge to change my life forever.

Throughout the summer, I followed the news reports of the draft, the Marines deploying to Da Nang, and the escalating conflict. I began to look for ways out. Although I was attending college, I could not afford to go to school full-time, so I knew it was likely I would be drafted unless I acted boldly. I watched as my friends began to disappear. First there were the guys from high school: Jimmy Dorsey, Paul Dent, and Bill Sutton. Others, more fortunate, sought and received deferments. Some got married hoping that it would spare them. It did not. I continued to look for ways to avoid the draft and hoped my job would spare me.

At the time, I was working for the Central Intelligence Agency (CIA) as a mail and file clerk. I approached them but learned that mail clerks were not essential to national security. Soon guys I worked with began taking induction physicals; Robert Simmons, Mickey Douglas, Ronald Simpson, Melvin Chase, and James Hart all went for their physicals the same day. Those guys were a year older than me, so I knew my time was close.

In July 1965 as my twentieth birthday passed, I considered enlisting. I knew by enlisting, I could at least escape Vietnam, if not the service. I began talking to recruiters. In August, when the size of the draft pool got larger, I made the decision to enlist in the Navy. Looking back, I can see now that the decision had been easy. My oldest brother Francis had been in the Navy nearly ten years; my mother, Rachel Butler, was working for the Navy; and I had other relatives serving in the Navy as well. Besides, I rationalized then, it would be better to curse myself for making a bad decision than to allow a worse fate by doing nothing. I would leave for the Naval Training Center, Recruit Training Command, Great Lakes, Illinois, on October 20, 1965.

To celebrate my going into the Navy, I threw a party on the Friday before I reported for active duty. All of my friends from the CIA, State Department, National Security Agency, and Defense Intelligence Agency came to my little apartment on Astor Place in Southeast Washington, DC to say their goodbyes. Because of the size of the turnout, I soon ran out of beer and scurried to the store to get more. When I returned, one of the revelers, my sister Joanne, said someone special was waiting to see me. To my surprise, who should it be but Rachel Morrissey, the young lady I had met earlier that year whom I assumed I would eventually marry.

The Navy

As the commercial jet landed at Chicago's O'Hare Airport on that October 1965 morning, I did not know what to expect of the nearby naval training base. There were eight buses waiting to take us from O'Hare field to the base. Later I would learn that our buses were the spearhead of an increasing contingent of sailors being pushed through three Navy Recruit Training Centers and out into the fleet.

At the base, they divided us into companies and began processing us into the Navy. Processing was a real wake-up call. The first thing we heard from our company commander, a Gunner's mate, Petty Officer First Class James Jewel, was a string of profanities that ended with, "...and I want your sex books, matches, knives, guns, condoms, razors, drugs, and anything else your mother gave you before you left home this morning." He continued, "If I don't get your sex books, matches, knives, guns, condoms, razors, drugs and whatever else your mother gave you, I'll send you home looking so different your mother won't recognize you. Am I making myself clear?"

Needless to say, the time (1:00 a.m.), his demeanor, and our being bone-tired, made his threats seem more sinister than they were. Somehow, I felt ashamed at not having any of the specified items. The next morning started rudely at 5 a.m.–boot camp had officially begun.

Basic training was rather uneventful, with the exception of my being tagged a nonqualified swimmer (NQS) because I could not swim the length of an Olympic-sized pool. Officially, we were Recruit Company 625. To other companies we were Jim's Jewels, a reference having nothing to do with precious stones. At first, the name provoked fights. But, by the time we finished Basic, we had accepted it as a badge of merit, competing to see who was the best of the gems. Petty Officer Jewel liked it too, saying, "You guys have earned the name because you're screwing all the other companies out of their awards." We graduated Basic Training with honors.

While at Great Lakes, I could always count on getting mail from the two Rachels in my life: my mother Rachel and Rachel Morrissey. At times, theirs were the only letters I received, and both were a welcome treat. In November, however, a month after enlisting, I received my draft notice. During the fall of 1965, the Army took the lion's share of the draft pool and, I am told, 60% went into the infantry. Had I not had the foresight to enlist, I would have been caught in that pool, too. I thanked my lucky stars that I had enlisted.

As a joke, I made a copy of the notice and sent it to a friend, Cliff Holland, who had somehow managed to avoid the draft. It scared the hell out of him until he read my enclosed letter explaining the joke. He didn't think it was funny.

CHAPTER TWO

The *Fox*

After boot camp and a short visit home for Christmas, I reported to the Norfolk Naval Shipyard, Norfolk, Virginia, for duty on board the USS *Douglas H. Fox* (DD-779). The *Fox* was built in Todd Shipyard in Seattle, Washington, and launched in September 1944. It was commissioned the day after Christmas 1944 and was named for Lieutenant Commander Douglas H. Fox, U.S.N., winner of two Navy Crosses for heroism. He lost his life during the battle of Guadalcanal while commanding the destroyer USS *Barton* in 1942. At the time I reported aboard, the *Fox* had just returned from a deployment to the Mediterranean.

I arrived in Norfolk at 11:30 p.m. and went to the Naval Operations Base (NOB). At the gate, I learned that the *Fox* was not at NOB but in dry dock at the Naval Shipyard, Portsmouth, Virginia, about four miles away. This would not have been too bad if it had been daytime and I was driving. But it was late at night and I was on foot, trying to hitch a ride while carrying a sea bag full of clothes. It took me another hour and a half to get there.

When I got to Portsmouth, what a let down! As a city kid, I had never seen a ship, let alone warships in dry dock. The *Fox* sat out of the water on chocks, the furthest out of three ships tied abreast. She was decked out in red lead paint, operating on electrical power from ashore, and reeking of stale sweat, paint, and diesel fuel from the many motors cluttering the deck and dry dock.

In an attempt to make the best of what appeared to be a worsening situation, I stuck out my chest in my finest military manner and crossed the quarterdeck of the first and then the second ship. At the *Fox*, I asked for permission to come aboard.

The grungiest sailor in the rattiest dungarees, with a Colt .45 pistol strapped to his hip, limply returned my salute and growled at me, "Set your f—king sea bag down and wait over there off my quarterdeck." He sent for the messenger of the watch who then took me to the berthing compartment.

In the darkness, I could not see beyond the glow of the messenger's flashlight but I could hear snoring. He led me to what appeared to be a black hole (a lower rack) and told me to bunk down there for the night.

The morning came fast. When I awoke, I was appalled to see what I had been lying on, a yellowish-brown mattress cover soiled with awful stains. I felt sick. I showered, dressed, and boarded the bus to breakfast at the mess hall on the other side of the shipyard.

Our bus driver, a sailor, loved racing with the shipyard cranes. What seemed to make him happiest was beating the crane to the turn in the road. On most mornings he made it, but one morning he did not. The crane hit the door of the bus, jammed it closed, hooked it, and began dragging us along the track. As we approached the edge of one of the dry docks, someone finally got the crane operator's attention. With great effort, we managed to force the door of the bus open. Of course, by the time this happened we had missed morning muster. As a result, all of us were restricted to the ship for a day because no one had mentioned the sailor's reckless driving to the captain. From then on, as further punishment we had to walk across the shipyard to breakfast.

Life on the *Fox* was an eye opener. As a straight-laced twenty-year-old, I saw the real underbelly of destroyer life. During my six months onboard, I was assigned to the deck force–cleaning, painting, and

generally helping to maintain the ship's exterior.
During that time, I saw sailors attempt to kill each
other over simple things: money, alcohol, drugs, and
prostitutes. Ironically, the animosity never seemed to
last long. Between paydays, things settled down. But
then on payday, the cycle of violence would start
again. I was appalled by that lifestyle and could hardly
wait to get off the ship.

The environment the sailors lived in was
conducive to that lifestyle. Downtown Norfolk was a
bastion of segregation. The area from the Greyhound
bus station at Brambleton and Granby Streets to the
waterfront was designated whites-only and included
much of downtown.

The heart of the black area started at Brambleton
and Church Streets and ran down Church to Princess
Ann Road. That two-mile stretch was crowded with
bars, greasy spoons, pool halls, and juke joints,
including Bob's Lounge, Top Side, Archie's, and the
Elk's Club. Most of the civilians who patronized those
places made a living selling the black sailors things
that reminded them of home. Some sold illegal and
illicit items. I had never seen anything like it.

Both civilian and military police patrolled the area
heavily. Abuse was rampant. It was not uncommon to
see police officers frisk women just for the sake of

copping a feel, or patting down a sailor for some minor infraction such as jaywalking. Because of these things, most weekends I went home to Washington. However, the absolute worst thing I saw while stationed onboard the *Fox* occurred on one of the few Saturdays I decided to stay in town.

That night, some of the other black sailors convinced me to join them. Despite my age, I was able to enter most of the bars along the strip because no one checked ID cards. It was about 11 p.m. and we had been drinking for about three hours. As we came out of one of the clubs, Price, a sailor in our group, bumped into one of the white police officers walking along the street. Immediately, the officer struck him with his baton. Price went limp and fell to the ground unconscious, blood pouring from his temple. Some of us rushed to his aid, trying to stop the bleeding.

As we bent down, the officer shouted, "Back away from him or I'll shoot you!"

One of the sailors stood up and asked, "Why did you hit him?"

With that, the officer pulled his revolver, cocked it, and pointed it at us. I froze. Before long, the street was filled with military and civilian police. One of the military policemen pushed me aside and grabbed the sailor who had confronted the officer. The police arrested everyone except me. They ordered me to move along, which I did.

When I returned to the ship, things were in an uproar because most of the black section of the deck force that had gone ashore that night had been arrested. As a result of the arrests, the duty officer had to go downtown to bail them out. Once the entire section was back onboard the *Fox*, we were restricted to the ship.

I later learned Price and that particular policeman had clashed several times before. For months they had been arguing back and forth, but the arguments had never before escalated to violence. Price normally just moved on, but this time the policeman took advantage of him. That one act of sudden, unprovoked violence made me pray daily for deliverance from the *Fox*.

Our restriction lasted only a week. Three days after the fight, we moved out of dry dock and began preparing for sea trials.

One of the first expressions I heard after joining the Navy was, "Sailors belong on ships and ships belong at sea." This adage proved true. As soon as the ship began preparations to leave dry dock, and later during sea trials, the mood among the sailors improved. Some still complained about the restriction, but most were anxious to get under way.

The day the ship was refloated, the captain treated the crew to a picnic on *steel beach* (the fantail of the ship). We had hot dogs, hamburgers, and bunny beer (nonalcoholic beer). The entire ship was upbeat. Four days later, we got under way for operations in the Virginia Capes area. I detected a certain sense of pride and camaraderie as we stood in formation along the rails while leaving port that morning.

I learned about being seasick when we cleared the port's mouth. My stomach felt queasy. I had no idea what was happening. Immediately, I started below to the berthing compartment to lie down. Before I cleared the hatch and got down the ladder, I made a beeline for the rails and retched. The longer I stood there, the more I retched. And the more I retched, the more I wanted to stand there.

I felt as if I were dying, but I heard giggling and laughter coming from the other side of the fantail. The more experienced sailors were laughing at me and others like me. They had placed bets to see which of the dozen or so new sailors would be the first to get seasick. I had won the derby!

It took me about a day and a half to recover. But I did learn a valuable lesson. For my subsequent twenty years with the Navy, I always made it a point to be asleep when we got under way. Sleep was the only thing that gave my inner ear time to adjust. I rarely got seasick again.

In the spring of 1966, my prayers for deliverance were answered. I left the *Fox* and was assigned to the Communications Technician "A" School at Bainbridge, Maryland. The classes, basic administrative assistant's courses, ran June through August and presented little challenge. However, the real beauty of the school was that it put me an hour away from home and two hours closer to Rachel Morrissey. Now my weekends were filled with Rachel and her hometown of Red Bank, New Jersey.

What I liked most about visiting her was the feeling of being at home. Her parents and the rest of her family trusted and liked me, both of which made me feel at ease. These feeling were things I had never before experienced outside of my family in Washington. I basked in their friendship and did my best to reciprocate.

In early August, I learned that I was being reassigned to England. At that time, I really didn't want my life disrupted again. Things were going well with Rachel, and I was beginning to know my way around the Navy. But here I was facing another drastic change in my life. I felt helpless.

The morning the orders came in, mine were among the first the staff yeoman read. In announcing them, he said, "Communications Technician Seaman Harold A. Butler, 914-67-19, you have orders to NAVSECGRUDET, CINCUSNAVEUR, NAVFAC, United Kingdom."

I had no idea what the Navy acronyms meant. During the class break I called my mother, who worked at Navy Headquarters in Washington, DC. When I told her about the orders, she laughed and said, "Sonny, you are going to London, England."

I felt both excited and sad. I was excited because, before I enlisted, I had been saving to go to Spain and knew I would get to realize that dream if I were stationed in England. I was sad because I feared it would take an inordinate effort to keep alive my budding relationship with Rachel.

Reluctantly, I wrote Rachel with the news. Instead of being sad, she, like my mother, was very happy that I was not going to Vietnam. Both knew the streets of London were safer than the rice paddies of Southeast Asia. They urged me to take care of myself. My father, on the other hand, was his usual stoic self, supporting my mother but not offering an opinion on my upcoming odyssey. I returned home to prepare for my departure.

I remember little of my days at home before leaving for England. I do know they were filled with packing and saying long goodbyes to my friends and my oldest brother Francis. During the spring of 1966, while I was still onboard the *Fox,* he and I began to develop a genuine brotherly friendship. He was stationed at the Brooklyn Navy Yard in New York, and whenever I would come to New Jersey, he made it a point to pick me up after I left Rachel. At the time Francis was dating his future wife, also named Rachel. He and I would laugh at the prospects of having three Rachels in our family, an idea particularly pleasing to Momma. We both knew being stationed near each other was a rare stroke of luck. What has become a lifelong friendship was sealed that summer.

Despite all the reasons for feeling good, I left Washington for New Jersey, en route to London, feeling very down.

Up to that point, 1966 had been full of new and exciting things. I had experienced a little of the Navy and liked it; I had begun to see New York and New Jersey; I had experienced things I never thought I would, like ice skating, ice sailing, and sledding; and I had eaten Coney Island hot dogs, Philly cheese steaks, and submarine sandwiches. I had assumed my entire four years in the Navy would be centered in and around the New York-New England area. The last thing I wanted was to leave those things behind.

On my last day in the States, I drove to Red Bank to see Rachel. It was a sad visit. We did what we could to make the best of it. We drove to the shore, walked along the river, ate more submarine sandwiches, cheese steaks, and hot dogs, and enjoyed each other's company. One of the last things we did was to go to Rachel's church, St. Thomas Episcopal, to see the picture of a sailor, Pervis Robison, whom I had been told I resembled. He had died tragically in 1963 when the USS *Thresher* SSN-593, a nuclear submarine, had gone down. Pervis Robison had been a friend of Rachel's family. In his honor the community placed a picture of him in the church as a memorial. I felt humbled being compared to him.

As I left Red Bank for New York, Rachel kissed me goodbye, smiled, and said with a giggle, "I will see you in the spring."

I turned, smiled, winked, and said, "Sure." At the time, I had no idea what she meant.

Despite the overwhelming sadness at leaving, in my heart I knew it was a good time. I was becoming a man and I was thoroughly infatuated with a beautiful young woman it had taken me a year to get to know. It was also an innocent time. And, despite my sadness, it was a great time for two twenty-one-year-olds who were falling in love with life, the world, and each other.

✧ CHAPTER THREE ✧

Douglas House

Between 1946 and 1960, the people of England had managed to vanquish from the landscape most of the visible signs of the devastation of World War II. London, in particular, had removed all its surface scars. Now, in the sixties, as the Vietnam War burst onto the front pages of American newspapers, a quieter, more subtle, social and sexual revolution was beginning in England.

Several factors fueled this new revolution: the immense severity of the post-war years; an increase in spending power of the average Brit; and an awakening of the British youth to the fact that, like their American cousins, they too could lead lives different from their parents.

In the fifties, the teenagers in England tended to act like little adults. Their dress, manner of speaking, and general conduct and demeanor clearly cast them as miniature Englishmen eagerly awaiting their proper place in society. In the sixties, post-war taboos had lifted. Those who might have been previously perceived as little adults found themselves free to act out their passions and desires. As a result, with the introduction of the contraceptive pill, legalized abortion, and the general lifting of the inhibitions and limitations of previous generations, *free love* became a part of life for many. And they openly pursued an agenda that allowed them, in the words of the time, to *get their groove on.*

Such was the backdrop for those of us who managed to avoid the Vietnam War and find ourselves in England. The period, the social events, and the war in Vietnam all became inextricably intertwined in a way we never could have imagined. For us, the Vietnam War raged a world away: we did not smell the gunpowder; we did not hear the wailing of the war sirens; we had no fear of booby traps or napalm; and we slept on clean sheets, not in foxholes. However, the social and sexual revolution was taking place all around us.

The most disruptive thing we encountered had been the draft. And, in our minds, we had prevailed. The war had little direct impact on our lives beyond the headlines of the morning paper. Despite this, the ripple effects of the draft, the war, and those times changed us dramatically. We were boys who became men as we served our country honorably from 1966 through 1968, even though we spent much of that time sitting on barstools in and around London and partying in the bowels of the American Servicemen's Club at #66 Lancaster Gate, London, W1, United Kingdom, a.k.a. Douglas House!

Douglas House, located just off Hyde Park, was a hotel that had been commandeered by the American forces and turned into an enlisted men's club. Its officer counterpart, Columbia House, was located a block away. Douglas House had a reputation for offering the best food, entertainment, and action America had to offer away from home.

Douglas House was fronted by two massive doors, one of which was always closed. As you entered, immediately to your right was a window where ID cards were checked. The first person you saw was seated at that window; for years, that person was a British woman named Jackie. She had beautiful fiery-red hair and always seemed to have something good to say. As one of the few people who could authorize visitors, she was an important person to get to know.

Just past Jackie, inside the front door to the left, was a sitting area where people awaited their guests. Past that area and also to the left was the main dining room. Across the hall from the dining room were the stairs. Downstairs were the barbershop, beauty salon, tailor shop, cleaners, and mini-commissary. Upstairs were the main bar, ballroom, and the slot-machine room.

The main ballroom was the place for dances, live shows, and, occasionally, bingo. It was there we got to see American rock-and-roll and rhythm-and-blues singers on tour with the USO. During my two years in London, I saw Carla Thomas and her dad, Rufus, BB King, Mary Wells, The Four Tops, Patti LaBelle, Tina Turner, The Coasters, and The Drifters. It was a great place to go because it offered a slice of home away from home, and best of all, the only price for admission was membership in the U. S. military.

The shows were impressive, major productions with elaborate costumes, and great local and traveling bands. They were better than anything you could get on the British market. As a result, admission to Douglas House was highly sought by non-Americans. Despite their opposition to the war in Southeast Asia, the Brits and other foreigners seemed not to mind this one form of Americana.

Most of the servicemen stationed in the London area patronized Douglas House. Some U.S. Air Force personnel would travel from bases as far away as Rislip and West Rislip (about thirty miles outside London) and Lakenheath and Bentwaters (more than an hour away). However, the trip to Douglas House for most sailors, marines, and soldiers was less than a fifteen-minute ride from their downtown London offices, a fact that irritated the airmen immensely–especially since Douglas House was operated and managed by American Air Force personnel. While other military services had their own clubs, they paled in comparison to Douglas House.

Englishmen and other foreigners operated the barbershop, tailor shop, cleaners, mini-commissary, and other service facilities. It was at Douglas House that the first nonblack person cut my hair. He was a Greek named Tony. He had been a barber during World War II and learned to cut black hair by practicing on the GIs on their way to fight Hitler. I was so shocked to learn a white man actually knew how to cut my hair that I wrote home about him. My parents thought I was being silly. A haircut from Tony usually cost no more than two dollars, including his tip.

When I arrived in London, I had been in the Navy almost a year. Although I had seen bars and clubs on bases in the States and in the Caribbean, Douglas House was beyond anything I had previously experienced. None of those other clubs had all the amenities, food, and entertainment under one roof like Douglas House. In addition, the happy hours started earlier than the other clubs, at 3:30 p.m., and they lasted until 7 p.m. Before happy hour, a rum and coke cost fifty cents; during happy hour, you got two rum and cokes for the same price. So, for a dollar, you could get four heavy rum and cokes and, since happy-hour food was free, you could eat all the sliced ham, chicken wings, hot dogs, and roast beef you wanted.

The food at Douglas House was excellent. The meals were typically American: large, fried, and full of gravy. My fondest food memories are of the oversized French fries, all-beef burgers with tons of cheese, and T-bone steaks. However, between paydays when you were broke, as I often was, the real staple of Douglas House was the homemade dinner rolls. They were free for the asking and made fresh daily. When added to a cup of free coffee, they provided enough nourishment to last you until lunchtime or through the night. Douglas House saved many of us from starving. I often wonder what would have happened to some of us if it had not been for the free happy-hour food and the homemade rolls.

The best feature about Douglas House was the women who came on Thursdays, Fridays, and Saturdays for happy hour and then stayed for the dances. Many were drop-dead gorgeous. Although most were Brits, they generally ran the rainbow in terms of color and style; ladies from the Middle East, the Caribbean, Europe, and Africa. All of them had a way of making you feel special. However, more than a few were merely retreads waiting for the next serviceman to come along. This scene was absolutely irresistible to a twenty-one-year-old man-child.

I was young, in a foreign country, and had Douglas House at my beck and call. It was akin to being let loose in a candy store. I enjoyed anything I desired, from food to alcohol to women. The only things that controlled me were my personal inhibitions and the desire to be faithful to the young lady I had left back home in the States. Those things, combined with my not understanding the rationale for blowing an entire two-weeks pay in one evening, helped to keep me in check most of the time. I failed on occasion, and I was not alone.

Most Fridays many of the marines, airmen, and sailors who patronized D–House had no dates, so we would congregate at the front door, hoping to escort a young lady into the club. Once they were signed in, if we were lucky, they would stay at our table all evening. But, more often than not, they would use us to get in, and then wait for their boyfriend who might be escorting someone else. If we were really unlucky, the boyfriend would come in by himself and threaten us for talking with his woman.

Although fights did occur, they were rare. There was a lot of posturing, but very few fights. During my tour in London, I can only remember two; they both included issues of race and women.

Black & White

Paydays were usually the time for excess drinking, bantering, posturing, and the rare fight. Servicemen would compete seriously for the attention of the women who came to the club. In some instances, the bantering and arguments were racially motivated. One particular weekend, the bantering turned into a serious argument that escalated into a fistfight and then a stabbing.

The event began when an English woman came to the club with her black boyfriend. In this particular case, the woman had both a black and a white boyfriend. While the men suspected the existence of each other, it wasn't until that evening they realized they were of different races.

When the white soldier came into the club, he saw her and was immediately furious, shouting, "How could you cheat on me with … *that?*"

Then he and the black soldier began arguing. As they shouted at each other, the story began to unfold. It became clear the woman had gotten her dates mixed. She thought her white boyfriend would be working all night, and therefore assumed it was safe to hang out with her black lover. She had it all wrong.

After the two men got tired of shouting, they began pushing each other. Then the white soldier made the *that* comment again, and the fight started. In the midst of the shouting, one guy pulled a knife. In self-defense, the other grabbed a steak knife from one of the surrounding tables. Just as they were about to go at each other, the young woman jumped between them and was stabbed in the shoulder. Blood flew everywhere!

The fight was over. Within seconds, the club was flooded with Air Policemen, and soon after, by British bobbies. While the woman was placed in an ambulance for transport to the local hospital, the police arrested the two servicemen. However, rather than incarcerate them, the police let them go; neither wanted to press charges. I was shocked at the stabbing, having never seen anything like it.

About a month later, all three of them were back in the club. They were celebrating what they called "our mishap." The entire affair made no sense to me.

The Aussie

Despite those rare events, usually Douglas House was a fun place to be. Occasionally a British or Australian serviceman would find his way into the club as a guest. Most of us knew nothing about them except their reputations as fierce fighting men.

One particular evening an American combat soldier brought in an Australian. The two had been members of a special combined-forces Ranger unit in Vietnam. According to them, in 'Nam their unit had been responsible for going behind enemy lines and engaging the Viet Cong and North Vietnamese regulars using guerilla tactics. All of this stuff was exciting to us garrison soldiers who saw the war as something that was happening over *there*.

As the liquor flowed, their stories of atrocities began to take on a competitive edge. The more they drank, the more detailed the stories became. The longer they talked, the louder they got. The louder they got, the more animated they became. The stories soon escalated into an argument. We were sure a fight would ensue. Before long they were standing toe to toe, yelling in each other's face, spittle flying.

The Aussie shoved his hand into his pocket to pull something out. People backed away in a hurry, expecting a blow to be thrown or a weapon to be drawn. However, instead of a punch or a weapon, the Aussie pulled out a green-brown pouch and said with his outback accent, "Top this, motherf—ker!" and threw the pouch on the counter.

You could smell the pouch from a couple of feet away. It was raunchy. As we craned our necks to see, the Aussie reached over and pulled the drawstring on the pouch, turned it upside down, and out plopped five slightly preserved but rotting human ears.

"These," he proclaimed with pride, "are from my first and last kills in 'Nam. You Yanks are so bleedin' tough, top that." No one could. So the ears lay there in all their putridness.

Club management heard what was going on, came up to the bar, put all of us out, and closed the club, citing the ears as a violation of sanitation codes. Some of us thought it was funny; that is, until we heard that everyone present had been barred from the club for a week.

Being barred from Douglas House was the worst of punishments. It meant you had no place to socialize. British pubs, while okay, charged high prices and usually closed by 11 p.m. Douglas House, on the other hand, was reasonably priced and stayed open until 1 a.m. British nightclubs were generally not an option.

They operated as private, members-only places and had daily admission fees for nonmembers. In most cases their membership fees were used for discriminating against non-Brits, particularly people of color.

✧ CHAPTER FOUR ✧
Moving On

Although life in England for the vast majority of us centered on Douglas House, there was plenty to do outside. I was first introduced to the variety of British life the day my plane landed in England.

I arrived in London on a Saturday morning, having traveled from New York with James Turner, another sailor from Chicago. He and I had been stationed together at Bainbridge, Maryland and had received our orders the same day. We agreed to meet at Kennedy Airport en route to London. Although we were glad to see each other, we flew the entire trip across the Atlantic talking very little. I did not know then but James, like me, was leaving his girlfriend behind.

When we arrived at Gatwick, just outside of London, no one met us. We roamed around the airport looking for a way to the city. At Gatwick, we first discovered fish and chips, bangers and beans, and, of course, Guinness Stout. In our roaming, we stumbled onto a U.S. military information desk. They arranged for us to take a military bus to Douglas House.

Douglas House was the drop-off point for all service personnel arriving in London for duty. At Douglas House, the receptionist called the Navy duty driver, who came to meet us. When he arrived he told us that no one had received our orders, and confessed he did not know what to do with us. No provisions had been made for hotel accommodations or other housing. He suggested we hang out at Douglas House until things got straightened out. There we sat in the lobby of a converted hotel, which even had rooms–but none for us.

Despite our having orders, we were considered stragglers, and stragglers were never allowed to stay at Douglas House. We could sit in the lobby until closing but we could not stay in any of the rooms. Fortunately, our wait lasted only six hours. Despite the sights and smells of Gatwick Airport, this intro-duction to England and the U.S. military overseas did little to quell my anxiety.

The Navy resolved the arrival debacle by placing us in a bed and breakfast (B&B) for a couple of weeks. The B&B was just off Bayswater Road near Hyde Park and about two miles from the office. I remember the place as musty, dank, and cold, and we had to share a bath with others. To our surprise, we learned there were some young Brits living next door who loved to party. Every day brought loud music and the continuous traffic of young women. At first we were a little leery of crashing, in part because of the continuous smell of marijuana emanating from the house. The sickeningly sweet smell of the stuff would waft through our windows all hours of the day and night as if the house were one continuously lit joint.

One evening, after watching boring British TV, which usually went off around 11p.m., we decided to crash one of their parties. At first the idea seemed great. As Yanks we were a welcomed novelty. However, our enjoyment ended when we discovered that one of the women was interested in James.

In letting him know that she liked him, she stated, "I hope my interest in you does not hurt your relationship with Harry."

To which James smiled and said, "Oh, he won't mind."

At first we were both pleased that one of us seemed to be making progress at meeting people. Then James noted that some of the guys were dancing only with each other. Likewise for some of the girls.

We decided to leave. Later when we compared notes, we laughed at the thought of us crashing a gay party.

Soon after, we found more permanent living arrangements. James moved in with other sailors who worked with him in the Reports and Publications Issue Office. I moved into another B&B in Kilburn on Willsden Lane.

The Willsden Lane B&B was owned and operated by two elderly men whom I later learned were gay. Mr. Stokes and Mr. Mack were old World War II veterans who made a living renting their rather large Victorian home to U.S. military families on a short-term basis. They were like Laurel and Hardy in both size and temperament. Mr. Stokes was Stan Laurel—fussy, slightly absent-minded, quiet, and somewhat eccentric. Mr. Mack was Oliver Hardy—big, boisterous, and bossy.

The day I moved in, Mr. Mack made it a point to let me know, "We took you in as a favor to some of the people in your office." He paused and then continued, "Your office had not expected a black, so they had not sought a place that would accommodate someone like you."

Discrimination in housing was an accepted practice in England. Despite this, I did enjoy my time at the Stokes place. I would have been content to stay longer because it was clean, comfortable, and cheap. However, their remarks, combined with other incidents, ultimately made living there unbearable.

When I arrived in England, I did not date at all for about three months. I preferred to stay in my room at the Stokes place in hope of the time passing quickly. After a while I got extremely lonely. In desperation, one day while on the job I called my mother at her office. My call startled and depressed her. But as soon as she realized I was making an illegal call, her sympathy turned to anger. She gave me hell and hung up. Subsequently, she wrote me about the foolishness of my actions and made me promise not to jeopardize my future in that manner ever again.

For the next month I dreaded picking up the office mail. I just knew that call would be on the phone bill. Fortunately, when the bill finally arrived, I got a lucky break. At the time, my mother worked for the Naval Ships' Engineering Center, abbreviated NAVSEC. My office was Naval Security Group, abbreviated NAVSECGRU. Because the two acronyms appeared so similar on the bill, the command assumed that NAVSEC was NAVSECGRU. I had dodged a bullet, but I learned my lesson. From then on, rather than sit, be lonely, and get in trouble, I decided to go out.

✧ CHAPTER FIVE ✧

Ivanna

Soon after that near-disastrous call to my mother, I met a young Jamaican lady named Norma Ivanna Franco. By now I had been in London about five months. From the moment we met, I told her about Rachel and my expectations when I returned home. As a result, Ivanna and I became friends only, and on occasion we would go out.

I met Ivanna at Count Suckle's Que Club on Curzon Street in Paddington, London. Que Club was the place where most young nonwhites went to party on the weekends. It was also the place where black military personnel could go to get away from what I was coming to realize was the less-than-subtle bigotry of some of our fellow white Americans and some Brits.

Que Club was in a converted cellar near Paddington Station. To enter, you descended a flight of concrete stairs that always smelled of urine.

Although I did not care much for the club because of its seedy location, it was a place to go after Douglas House closed. Additionally, it was one of the few places where women of color usually outnumbered white women.

The night I met Ivanna, she was wearing a brown high-collared dress that buttoned down the right side from the neck to her hemline. As a Jamaican Indian, she always wore her hair up in some variation of a French roll. Her dress, hairstyle, complexion, and seemingly demure demeanor made her one of the more attractive women in the club.

When I first asked, she refused to dance with me. However, after I persisted, she gave in. When it came time to leave, she gave me her number without my asking. Her forwardness surprised me; I had never had a woman just give me her number without my having to ask. I called her that week and asked her out to the movies. When I arrived, I was surprised to learn she had a son, Samuel.

Samuel was a rosy-cheeked little boy with sandy-brown hair and an impish grin. He loved watching *The Thunderbirds*, a children's show about pilots, on the telly and eating Wheatabix, a brand of British crackers. When I asked who was going to watch Samuel while we were at the movie, Ivanna responded, "I can't afford a sitter, so I guess no one." I insisted Samuel come with us. From that moment and for the next four months or so, Samuel and I were friends.

On Saturday mornings when I wasn't busy, he and I would go to the park or, if I had duty, to my office. It was because of him that I got to see the London Zoo. We also went to Battersea, an amusement park, where we had a good time.

I loved being with Samuel and cared about his mother, but I also knew the danger of getting too close. So I made it a point to keep my distance. Despite my not being interested in Ivanna sexually, she and I became good friends.

Like me, Ivanna was very lonely. She had just broken up with her son's dad. And, as a result of her unwed pregnancy, her family had disowned her. With the exception of her son and friend Beverly, she had few friends in England. Although Beverly would spend some time with her, most of Ivanna's time was spent working, caring for Samuel, and planning to go home permanently to Jamaica.

Ivanna lived near Shepherd's Bush Market, a large outdoor market stretching more than two blocks in London's West End. On those Saturdays when I would stop by to pick up Samuel, she would have a sandwich or a beer waiting for me. One day while

visiting her, I experienced an event that soured my
opinion of America and made me wonder about the
value of my presence in England.

That particular day, I was reading the newspaper
while waiting for Samuel to get dressed. Suddenly,
Ivanna shouted to me, "Harry, come here!"

Thinking something had happened to either her or
Samuel, I ran to the kitchen. When I got there,
Ivanna, pointing at the telly shouted, "Look, your
country is in flames."

There on British television were pictures of
soldiers from the 82nd Airborne Division standing
with fixed bayonets on the steps of what appeared to
be the U.S. Capitol, apparently there to protect the
building from protesters. Suddenly I was overcome
with sadness and could not speak. The only thought
running through my mind was, "Why am I here, if my
own people can't get along?"

Ivanna saw my reaction and apologized. It did not
help. I left without saying a word and went home,
wanting to be alone.

Ivanna never liked her flat in Shepherd's Bush. As
a result, she was always looking for a new place to live.
When I told her where I lived, she wanted to see my
room and inquired whether there might be other

rentals nearby. Innocently, I took her by the Stokes place. What a mistake!

After less than twenty minutes, I walked Ivanna back to the bus stop. When I returned Mr. Stokes invited me into the parlor. And there beside the roaring fireplace in one of the two overstuffed chairs in the room sat Mr. Mack. He asked me to sit down in another, straight-backed chair. He then reminded me in a very stern voice that they ran a reputable rooming house for families, reiterating that they were doing me a favor by letting, "… you, a single black man, stay here." Then he added, "We do not allow the likes of that sort to ever enter our establishment unless on official business. … Had you not been an American, you would not have darkened our door." Then, finally, he concluded in a somewhat less stern voice, "All Englishmen learn from a very early age, 'You don't shit on your own front door step.'"

I was furious and could not believe this was happening to me. All I could think was, "How insane. Here I sit in a stiff-backed chair being put in my place by two old fags (living as husband and wife) and all because I had the audacity to bring *that sort* to their house."

I could not decide which hurt more, their bigotry or their hypocrisy. However, rather than lash out, I quietly gathered my belongings and went up to my room. Less than a week later I moved out. Although I got several messages at work that they were concerned about me, during the rest of my stay in England, I never went back to the Stokes place.

In January 1967, Ivanna received a letter inviting her and Samuel to come to New York. I encouraged her to take advantage of the opportunity, if not for herself, then for Samuel. Although I encouraged them to go and accompanied them to Heathrow the morning they left, as soon as they were out of sight, I cried. I knew that I would probably never see them again. Over time, I have missed Ivanna and have often wondered about them, particularly after the birth of Michele, my first child. Ironically, she and Samuel looked enough alike to have been sister and brother.

✧ CHAPTER SIX ✧

The Apartment

My first real flat was in Kensal Rise at #54 Leighton Gardens. To get the flat, which was on the top floor of a converted two-story house, I needed a roommate to help with the rent, which was thirty three pounds (£33) or nearly $90.00 per month. John Williams, another black sailor, agreed to be my roommate.

John hailed from Georgia. At nineteen, he was among the youngest of the sailors stationed in London. He stood almost six feet tall and weighed approximately 220 pounds. As roommates, we could not have been more different. He wanted to party, go to the club every day, pick up women, and drink. I was primarily interested in getting my college education, only occasionally meeting women, and drinking. To him the week was made to party. I reserved my partying for the weekend.

We lived above the landlady, named Shirley, who was a bleached blonde and a real good-time girl. She and her girlfriend, UK Rose, a rather manly looking redhead, were regulars at Douglas House and other clubs patronized by U.S. servicemen. UK Rose got her name because she allegedly slept with anyone and everyone (willing or not) who arrived in the UK.

After we moved in, I found that Shirley's house was regarded as a neighborhood nuisance. During the week, she arranged card parties. On the weekend, she had selling parties: liquor, food, women, you name it. I must have been the only person stationed in London who had not been there before I moved in.

The flat at #54, like most of the places in England at that time, had no central heating. It lacked caulking around the windows and doors, so it was drafty and cold. It came furnished with an old overstuffed sofa and matching chairs, older dining room furniture, and even older, but usable, bedroom furniture. Despite all this, I was happy because it was a place away from Mr. Stokes and Mr. Mack and their insistence that I behave like a good Englishman, discreet but perverted.

During my time at #54, I witnessed numerous arguments, fights, and several unsavory business deals (sexual and otherwise). As a result, at the end of my first month in the flat, I was ready to move. The straw that broke the camel's back was the night I came home from classes and found Rose, John, and Shirley drinking my tenth of Johnny Walker Black.

Growing up in Washington, I believed I knew what it took to be a good host. Part of being a good host was keeping a stash of special liquor for your really special friends. For me that special stash was the tenth of Johnny Walker Black scotch. To ensure its safekeeping, I kept it on the mantel over the fireplace in my bedroom.

When I came in from classes that night, I made it a point to avoid going into the living room with the three of them. But as I passed the door, I happened to notice a bottle of scotch in the middle of the coffee table. Then I noticed that my bedroom door was ajar. I pushed open the door and to my surprise, found the mantel was empty. Fuming, I flew down the hall and confronted John.

He was apologetic and promised he would pay me back. In addition, I insisted he get Rose and Shirley out of the flat. The request brought Rose and Shirley to their feet, and they began to berate John for not defending their honor.

John replied, "You bitches, you can't even spell the word *honor*."

With that, Rose pushed John, and Shirley jumped on his back. The next thing I knew, they were in the hallway pushing and shoving. John lost his footing and with Shirley on his back, slipped and slid down the stairs, pulling Rose after him. They landed at the bottom of the stairs with a big thud. At that, I laughed, then closed and locked the door.

For the next couple of minutes they screamed and yelled at each other. Then someone laughed and, the next thing I knew, John was inviting me to come down for a "make-up" drink. I told them all to go to hell.

The Assault

The physical and verbal conflicts we had that first month with Shirley and Rose were nothing compared to an incident that could have cost me my life. That day, a Sunday, started like most other Sundays. John and I had slept late and were passing time before going out. We both had dates. I had planned to go to the club for brunch with Ivanna. John was meeting Irene, his future wife, to go to the movies. We had just finished showering and getting dressed. I was standing in front of the floor-length mirror in the living room when John shouted, "Hey look bro, there is an SOB stabbing the shit out of this bloke."

Knowing that John loved to kid people, I laughed and said, "Yeah, sure."

But then I casually walked over to the window, and it was just as John had said. Two Englishmen were fighting, one stabbing the other with upward thrusts. Each stab seemed to lift the other man off the ground. I knew enough to know that those kinds of stabbing motions were killing motions. I shouted to John, "Hey, we can't let that happen."

We ran down the stairs and out onto the streets where a crowd had gathered to watch the fight. Instinctively, I grabbed the man being stabbed and pushed him behind me. As I did, John handed me a knife and said, "Take this, it's for you!"

I told him I did not need it and threw it away. By then the other bloke was approaching me, as if to stab me. I backed up fully fixated on the knife, expecting to be stabbed. But to my surprise, he stopped, turned, ran to his car, got in, and drove away.

With the assailant gone, I turned my attention to the stabbing victim. He was bleeding profusely, pacing, and babbling. As he walked back and forth, he began to cry and talk to himself. Then he began to talk to me. He talked about his children, his wife, and how much he loved them. He talked about the day being a bad day to die. He wanted to know who would take care of his children. He asked, "Will you tell my parents how I died?"

Out of frustration and not knowing what else to say, I shouted, "I'll be damned if you're going to die!"

We coaxed him inside Shirley's flat and after a while, got him to lie down. Then in the middle of Shirley's living room, we began to render first aid.

I asked John to get some towels. As the victim lay there, I unbuttoned his shirt. His chest was covered with blood. His left nipple had been completely severed. His right nipple was split in two. He had at least a dozen wounds on his chest and abdomen.

As we stood over him, John and I wiped his chest with the towels. We didn't dare kneel down; there was just too much blood. I suggested to John that we move him because he was lying in a pool of blood. When we put our arms around his upper back, I pulled away with a handful of blood. We decided to roll him over instead. Then we discovered he had as many puncture wounds in his back as were in his chest. Then I tried to move him back. But as I moved him, I noticed my shoes, crepe-soled boots, were stuck to the floor. I got sick to my stomach, felt light-headed, and nearly threw up.

About twenty-five minutes later, the British ambulance service arrived and took over. Within minutes of the ambulance, the police arrived. They questioned John and me extensively. It was during the interrogation we learned the stabbing had occurred because the victim had come to Shirley's house looking for his wife, whom he heard was meeting her boyfriend there. The poor man had walked in on the two of them and gotten stabbed for his efforts. The police questioned us for about an hour.

Later that week, British Criminal Investigation Division (CID) came to the office to talk to us. Of course, the Navy wanted to know the full story. We told them, and they allowed us time off to go to court. Officially the Navy never acknowledged what we did. In retrospect, I have seen others get medals for much less. We got nothing. No thank you for risking our lives, no congratulations for being good citizens. Nothing!

A month after the stabbing, John and I did appear in court. Just as in the movies, there sat the judge and all the barristers with their powdered wigs and flowing robes. And into the midst of this scene came the two colored American sailors, ready to testify.

As luck would have it, I was called to the stand first. The Queen's Counsel asked me if I recognized the victim. I stated I did. Then he asked me if I could identify the assailant. I replied, "I can not because I was focused on the knife he was wielding." However, I offered to identify the knife, which I did.

The judge said to me, "Mr. Butler, the Crown thanks you for your courage and assistance. You are dismissed." I sat down at the back of the court with the other witnesses and spectators. Then it was John's turn.

The Queen's Counsel asked John the same questions. When John began to answer, Counsel stopped him and corrected him based upon John's statement to the police. He asked John a second and third question, and each time John said something contrary to his original statement. Finally, the Queen's Counsel asked John a fourth question and reminded him of his statement to the police, to which John replied, "Hell, if you got my motherf—king statement, why are you asking me all these dumb-ass questions?"

I was flabbergasted. The judge was stunned. Then he and all of the attorneys began to laugh and laugh. The sight of the powdered wigs nearly sliding off the heads of the judge and the attorneys made me giggle too.

Finally, the judge thanked us and sent us on our way. As we stopped at the clerk's desk to pick up our two-pound stipend for court service, I asked John why he had made us look so foolish. John's only explanation for his outburst was, "The SOB pissed me off!"

A couple of weeks after the stabbing, one of the neighbors introduced me to a Jamaican woman who owned a house at #44 Leighton Gardens. I moved and reluctantly took John with me.

The house at #44, like the one at #54, was an older World War II British row house, with two stories and no basement. As you entered, there was a minor vestibule and then a flight of stairs that led to the top floor. This time our flat was on the bottom floor.

Although the house had indoor plumbing, it had coin-operated meters for the hot water and electricity. They operated on shillings. A single shilling (around 28 cents) got you about fifteen minutes of hot water. Ten shillings (a pound) got you enough hot water to last about two days.

To get to the backyard, you had to go through the kitchen. The backyard was fairly typical of most yards in Britain. It was between 25 and 30 feet wide by 40 feet long, overgrown with weeds.

John and I agreed to split the expenses on the house down the middle. However, I learned that he could not and would not cook. Although he paid his half of the rent on time, he was usually broke or nearly broke the rest of the time. He was not the most reliable person in the world.

✧ CHAPTER SEVEN ✧
The Milk Bandits

We spent a great deal of our energy in England trying to hold on to money while staving off hunger. As young men who barely knew how to survive on our own, we were just learning the intricacies of basic budgeting. Although we tried hard not to, sometimes we still ran short between paydays. Out of necessity and fear of starvation, we found ways to compensate.

One of the things we did was to take advantage of some fine, old British traditions. One such tradition was the milkman's daily delivery of a fresh pint of milk to many doorsteps. For the better part of a month, we would follow the milkman's route as it progressed towards the tube station near our house.

As the milkman made his deliveries along High Road, we would hide in the bushes or behind rubbish bins, out of sight, waiting for him to deposit the milk on a doorstep. Once deposited, we would

pounce, consuming most of the milk along that
portion of his route.

This fresh milk, combined with the occasional
pilfering of freshly baked bread along the same route,
made for some of the best free eating a hungry, short-
of-cash GI could get.

All of this came to a screeching halt when the
local police arrested a couple of GIs for similar antics.
As if to further embarrass them, they were deported to
America to serve time as members of what the local
papers labeled a brazen, organized milk-stealing ring.
Amazingly, we all got better at budgeting after those
arrests. I've often imagined those poor guys in jail,
trying to explain to their fellow convicts that they were
in the company of milk thieves.

Give A Boy A Bone

Earlier I mentioned how much I enjoyed spending
spare time at the open-air markets in and around the
city. They provided a window to the diverse popula-
tions that were beginning to comprise greater London.
Along Kilburn High Road, there were so many
Pakistani and Indian shops that you almost felt you
were in Karachi or New Delhi. In Brixton, there were
so many West Indians, Asians, Africans, and Middle

Easterners living along the main road that at times you forgot you were in Europe.

Between paydays, those shops took on a practical purpose. Because budgeting was a constant problem for most of us, we were constantly searching for a place to beg, steal, or borrow food or money. Most times, it was a matter of a few of us scouring our cupboards and putting together a potluck stew. On other occasions, we had to be a little more creative.

One of the first things I noticed when I got to England was how their eating habits differed. What we called bacon and what they called bacon were two different things. While American bacon was thin and lean, British bacon tended to have more fat with mere streaks of meat. Their hot dogs seemed to have more filler and were closer to sausages than their American counterpart. In addition, the British rarely ate neck bones, chitterlings, pig's feet, or ribs. Exploiting those differences helped us when we had to scrounge for food between paydays.

One of our more successful food exploits, at least initially, took place on a Saturday while John and I were at Shepherd's Bush Market. We noticed that butchers threw away the tips of the beef and pork ribs. When we asked why, the butcher told us they were scraps only fit for the dogs. So we asked if we could have them. To our surprise, the guy gave us five pounds of them.

We took them home, boiled them, whipped up some homemade barbeque sauce, and baked them. For two months, we went by his shop and got all the free rib tips we wanted. One week we decided to show the butcher our concoction. At first he laughed at us for eating dog food. Then he tasted them. After one bite, he wanted to know how we made them; naively, we told him.

The following week, we stopped by his shop expecting more free ribs, but the butcher refused. As we left the shop, we learned that our big mouths had cheated us out of our source of free meat. Not only would the butcher not give us the ribs free, he was now calling them an American delicacy and was selling them for two shillings a pound.

Fortunately for us, there were other butcher shops in other markets.

CHAPTER EIGHT

The Funeral

In May 1967, I received word that my brother-in-law Raymond, a Marine Corps lance corporal, had been killed at Chu Lai, in the Republic of South Vietnam. Raymond's death was a complete surprise, coming in the last month of his thirteen-month tour of duty. He was killed by what the Marines called a toe popper, a land mine.

At first, I thought I could overlook his death, but as the days went by, all I could think of was my sister Janyce. The more I thought of her, the more I wanted to return home. A week before Raymond's body was to arrive home, I requested and was granted leave. I flew out of Heathrow for Washington, DC, on El Al Airlines, Israeli national airlines. I arrived home wearing a herringbone wool suit on a hot sunny day. Since none of my British-made clothes were suitable for the U.S. mid-Atlantic Coast climate, I had to buy new clothes.

Raymond's body arrived home ten days late. Taking the delay as providence, I used the time to renew acquaintances. With the exception of Cliff Holland and a few friends from church, I did not see many of my friends. Most were too busy to see me. And those who did seemed to question my being home while there was a war going on. I began to wish that Raymond's funeral was over with. Psychologically, I prepared to go back home to England via Red Bank. However, before I could, the Six-Day War broke out in the Middle East.

When hostilities commenced, Israel militarized all El Al planes and that stranded me in Washington. It took an extra week to get an Air India flight. But before I left Washington, Israeli gunboats and planes fired upon and nearly sank the USS *Liberty* (AG-TR-5).

The near-destruction of the *Liberty* was personally hurtful. The ship took its heaviest hits in the classified communications spaces where Communications Technicians (CTs) worked. I was a CT and knew well one of those killed. Petty Officer First Class John Smith, USN, had worked with me when I first arrived in London. His death, following so closely on Raymond's, impressed upon me the fragility of life in the military. Before the *Liberty* incident, most of us CTs had considered sea duty as little more than an extended working cruise. With John's death, I had had enough of death and the sea. The pain I first felt when I learned of Raymond's death returned. All I wanted was to go home to England where life was safe and the wars were far away.

✧ CHAPTER NINE ✧
Return to England

When I finally got back to England, the office was operating on an at-sea wartime schedule. Bunks lined the hallways. All staff, both officer and enlisted, were on three-section, rotating watches, meaning that every third day one section went home while the other two remained overnight in the office. All meals were brought in.

Morale was particularly low because no one could believe Israel, an ally and friend, would deliberately harm one of our ships and cost us a shipmate. But it happened and America did nothing!

Upon my return, I also found an unpleasant surprise at the flat. John had not been home most of the time I was away. The house was a mess; the dishes were dirty, there was trash all over the place, and it smelled from being closed up.

It took me three days to finally catch up with John. That day, my first Saturday back, I went into the office and found John serving as the duty yeoman in the Command Center. He was wearing a dingy white shirt and faded black trousers.

When I asked him where he had been, his reply was, "Bro, I've screwed so many women since you left, I believe my ass is about to fall off!"

I laughed and told him to meet me at home. When I got to the house, I discovered the unpaid bills. The electricity and the heat were about to be cut off. And, worst of all, our 3-pounds-per-month rented television was about to be repossessed.

To add to all of this, Rachel was due to arrive in less than a month. The combination of events led to a rather heated argument. I asked him when he would help clean up. He suggested I get Rachel to help me. I went ballistic. I had had enough of his crap and I told him to leave. At the end of the week, John moved in with Irene.

John had a propensity for getting himself and others involved in things not to their liking. One evening seven of us (John, Fitz, Stan, Dean, West, Kip, and I) decided to go to the Kyklos Klub in West Hampstead.

West Hampstead is located in the West End of London near Kilburn, Cricklewood, and Cottage City.

West Hampstead has always been known as a place for pubs, late-opening/late-closing bars, and excellent private clubs. In the sixties in England, private clubs were a means of getting around the relatively early 11 p.m. closing time of the pubs. According to rumor, West Hampstead was also a gathering place for some of the most beautiful Middle Eastern and Asian women. So the group of us decided to go and see for ourselves.

The Kyklos Klub was as we had expected. In front was a line of people waiting to get in. Once inside, we found ourselves in a large open area with chairs and tables around the walls. In the center of the room a dance floor stretched under a disco- style reflective ball. At most of the tables sat women, beautiful women of color. They were Indian, Pakistani, Filipino, Vietnamese, and a handful were West Indian.

We had never been to a club with such feminine variety. And, just as exciting, they all seemed to be friendly. We laughed because even the clubs around Piccadilly, known for their attractive women, paled in comparison. In the midst of all this, there was one problem; the club had more than its share of Englishmen and few men of color.

Before transferring to London, my uncle Bill had warned me about the Englishmen and their attitudes

towards black American GIs. He had been stationed
in London during World War II, and he told me a few
stories about his war years in London. Most of his
stories ended with the same admonition, "British men
generally do not like the Yanks, particularly the black
Yanks, because as the Brits used to tell it, 'They are
overpaid, oversexed, and over here. So be careful!'"

My own impressions indicated that many of the
Brit men still held to that notion. When we noticed
there were many more Brits than men of color, I antic-
ipated a difficult time. And problems started less than
an hour after our arrival.

When we entered, some of the guys wanted to
leave right away because they noticed the Brits seemed
agitated by our presence. However, Fitz and I insisted
we stay, me because I had managed to get one of the
Pakistani women to talk to me. Before long we were
dancing. When the music ended, as we remained in
the middle of the dance floor laughing and talking,
suddenly a Brit pushed between us, glared at her, and
called me a bastard. I told him to bug off, and he
walked away.

As I turned back to the young lady, John pushed
past the two of us and grabbed the guy, insisting he
apologize. I told John to forget it.

But John shouted, "If you don't apologize, I'll put my foot so far up your ass, you are going to need a surgeon to get it out!" At that, the young lady ran away.

I shouted to John, "Man, let it go!"

But it was too late. The Brit suggested we take it outside. As we came out of the club, there standing in the street was not only the guy John had grabbed, but also ten of his friends. Under the brighter streetlights, I got a good look at the guy John had confronted. He was somewhat stocky and had scars on his face that looked like ruts. His appearance clearly suggested he was someone who just might like fighting for the sake of fighting.

He and John were standing toe-to-toe arguing in front of a liquor store. In the store's window was a diamond-shaped display made with stacked liquor bottles. As John yelled at the Brit, one of the other guys with us, Kip, hit the bloke so hard he fell into the plate-glass window. While the window shook, all the display items on the other side of the glass fell. The fight was on!

The crowd surged up the street. Many punches were thrown, but no one was seriously hurt. The noise grew louder. In the midst of the din, we realized that our Brit foes had disappeared. The remaining few had drifted with us to the front of the West Hampstead

Police Station. Before we knew it, we were surrounded
by bobbies about to enter the fray. One of the bobbies
grabbed six-foot-five-inch Henry West.

This sight struck me as funny because the officer,
about five-feet-three-inches tall, had to stand on
tiptoes to grab West by the back of the collar. West,
feeling someone pulling on him, spun around, ready
to hit the first person he saw. As he turned, I grabbed
his arm and shouted, "West, don't!"

West stopped. Furious, the bobby turned toward
me. I backed up because I knew that if anyone of us
touched the officer, all of us would be in really big
trouble. Two reasons: first, some bobbies were known
for provoking fights and then beating people up; I was
alert enough to peg these cops as fitting that bill.
Second, I also knew that if we fought them, all of us
would likely be deported.

As I stood there pulling on West, the short bobby
spoke up, saying in a barely intelligible cockney, "'Ere
mate, let the motherf—ker go!" He continued, "'Ere,
'ere, I said let 'im go!"

The sound of his voice nearly made me laugh. But
I did as he said.

As I let West go, the bobby began unbuttoning his
tunic and, looking directly at West, asked, "Hey, mate,
do you want to 'ave a go?"

West said nothing.

Again, the bobby asked, "Hey, you such a bad nigger? Let's 'ave a go!"

West backed away. The bobby and his partners grinned, laughed out loud, then said, "Chicken-shit Yanks!" With that the fight ended.

The bobbies ordered us to follow them. They led us to the nearest bus stop, about half a block away. They waited for the bus to come, watched as we boarded, then told us if they ever saw our "arses" in West Hampstead again, they would kick the shit out of us. We got on the bus and thanked our lucky stars. As the bus pulled away, we waved at the bobbies and laughed.

As the bus rounded the corner, someone noticed that John was nowhere to be found. During the fight, somehow he had managed to slip away. Later we learned he had gone to a girlfriend's house two blocks away from the club. Around the time the confrontation with the bobbies heated up, John was sitting down in the young lady's living room opening a beer.

When John showed up, the only comment he made was, "Hey bro, you guys seemed to have everything well in hand, so I figured why hang around just for the sake of a bunch of cops itching to start a fight?"

Gerald A. Collins

✧ CHAPTER TEN ✧
The Oak Room

While fighting was actually rare, subtle discrimination was a fact of life in sixties London. This sometimes contributed to making a tenuous situation worse. One such instance involved a private club called The Oak Room. The Oak Room was about four doors down from Douglas House. It routinely refused admission to black Americans and other minorities, so we steered clear. However, its proximity to Douglas House made it difficult to ignore.

The Oak Room, like other private clubs, did not open until after 11 p.m. While most of the other private clubs that did not care for minority patrons made their policy known by charging exorbitant admissions fees, The Oak Room took the matter a step further. Not only did they charge nearly four times the normal admission fee, they also watered down the drinks served to people of color foolish enough to pay

these exorbitant prices. The entire affair came to a
head in April 1968,the month Dr. Martin Luther King
was killed.

Within days of the King slaying, several white
service members began praising the killing. It was not
uncommon at the office and in the club to hear whispered comments like, "They finally got that bastard,"
or "It's a good thing they killed that troublemaker." At
first, most of us said nothing, preferring to ignore the
remarks. But as time went on, the talk became more
public. It came to a head one evening when a black
sailor attempted to enter The Oak Room with a white
coworker and was told, "You could end up dead like
that SOB King."

Furious, the sailors left The Oak Room, came
back to Douglas House, and related what had
happened. Before long, a group of airmen, sailors,
and soldiers gathered at the entrance to The Oak
Room, intent on getting in. When we were quoted the
usual exorbitant admission fee, one of the guys cursed
the doorman and pushed past him. Before the
doorman could recruit backup bouncers, enough of us
had overwhelmed them to the point they had to call
the police. When the bobbies arrived, they ordered us
to leave. We refused, telling them we wanted to speak
to American military authorities. By this time, the

police outnumbered the twelve U.S. military personnel
by at least 2 to 1. Rather than force us to leave the
club, they called the Navy duty officer. We explained
the situation to him and insisted the club change its
policies. When he told us there was nothing he could
do, the chant went up, "Close the f—ker down!"
Hearing this, the duty officer promised us he would
report the matter and have the Command look into it.
With that we left.

The following week, the American authorities and
the British Criminal Investigation Division questioned
several of us about the incident. Despite the questioning, we were insistent that The Oak Room had to
change its policies. Some of us were threatened with
administrative punishment and, in one case, a court
martial. But we stuck to our guns, letting Command
know that if they did nothing, we would.

In the midst of this investigation, the Air Force
Command, followed by the Navy, made The Oak
Room off-limits to all U.S. military personnel. That
proved to be the straw that broke the proverbial
camel's back. Within two weeks of being placed off-
limits, The Oak Room lifted its discrimination policy.
Despite the change, few blacks patronized the club.

The Oak Room never recovered from the incident.
Less than a year after my transfer, in late 1968, The

Oak Room closed its doors permanently. As far as I am concerned, it was good riddance. I suspect that our single act of defiance caused The Oak Room's demise.

✧ CHAPTER ELEVEN ✧
Going Out

The best place for American food was Douglas House. It specialized in steaks, spaghetti and meatballs, chicken wings, ham, roasts, and baked and fried chicken. The food was plentiful, reasonably priced, and reminiscent of home. Near Douglas House, in the area around Nottinghill Gate, there were several very good Greek and Chinese restaurants. The remaining restaurants specialized in British staples: steak and kidney pie, shepherd's pie, and meat and potatoes, all of which were hearty but not too tasty.

My favorite Brit food was fish and chips. It tasted *so-o-o* good piping hot from the fryer, dripping grease, wrapped in brown paper, then wrapped in newspapers.

Then I fell in love; I discovered West Indian cooking. My favorite is still flying fish with red beans and rice. The absolute best place for good West Indian food, short of being invited to someone's home, was in the area of Labroke Grove, also fairly close to Douglas House.

There were several pubs and restaurants near the office I enjoyed also. My favorite was the Barley Mow, behind the office in the court just off Oxford Street. Near the house in Kensal Rise was the Red Lion. Like the Barley Mow, the Red Lion had a neighborly Brit atmosphere. They specialized in the usual British fare but also served some of the best bangers (a hot dog) to be had.

For mid-afternoon or lunchtime romance, you could not beat the ambiance of the restaurant in the basement of the American Embassy. It was a great place to go because it afforded privacy and an intimate atmosphere. Except for the Marine standing guard nearby, you almost got the feeling you were in some exotic nightspot. Like Douglas House, the Embassy's prices for food, beer, and wine were very reasonable.

In the general vicinity of Douglas House was Queensway Road. Near the office was Bayswater High Road. I mention them because, although they both had nice restaurants, they were better known as places to meet other young people, particularly young women. On Bayswater High Road, there was Wimpies, a British version of McDonalds. The hamburgers were lousy but it was a great place to get a Stout and meet an occasional East or West Indian lady who did not mind Americans.

Queensway, like Nottinghill Gate, offered a place to roam, drink cappuccino, and pretend to be cosmopolitan. It also sported great places for after-date drinks or just whiling away a lazy Saturday. Just off Nottinghill Gate was Portobello Road. Like Shepard's Bush, Hammersmith, and Pettycoat Lane, Portobello was the place for hundreds of open stalls, mini-shops, and some of the best open-stand cooking in and around London. I became particularly fond of Shepard's Bush and Portobello because they were great places to roam and lose myself when I got lonely or homesick.

Shows

London was the place for live theater, musical shows, and movies. On really special occasions, I would go to The Talk of the Town to catch the Supremes, The Four Tops, or The Temptations. Or I would go to The Royal Albert Hall to see Lou Rawls or Tony Bennett. However, due to my constant money shortage, I spent a great deal of time at the Odeon cinemas. Despite money problems, there were plenty of small clubs featuring struggling American artists. It was not uncommon to find Ike and Tina Turner, The

Drifters, The Coasters, Ramsey Lewis, or a myriad of other American musicians who flocked to England to investigate the Fab Four phenomenon.

✧ CHAPTER TWELVE ✧
Getting Around

I generally got along with most Brits because they seemed fascinated with me and my colleagues whom they referred to as black Yanks. I would typically meet them in my travels around London on public transportation. On the whole, they were standoffish, but still cautiously friendly and willing to help. I rarely ran across anything but politeness while using the buses, taxis, the tube, or the gypsy cabs.

Cabbies

Jamaicans and Africans usually operated gypsy cabs. Hansom cabs were generally the domain of Englishmen and the occasional Indian. Gypsy cabs were privately owned cars hired out by their owners. On a late night when the hansom cabs would either not pick you up or had stopped running, the gypsies could be a godsend. They would take you anywhere in

London. They were generally a reliable and trouble-free mode of transportation. However, occasionally they became a problem when the drivers discovered you were an American.

The troublesome drivers would take you to your destination, want to socialize with you, and then charge you for waiting. They would also try to take advantage of you because they thought you might be drunk.

Overcharging and their wanting to socialize were the least of the problems with the gypsies. Many of them drove on suspended licenses or, worse yet, no license. On more than one occasion, I found myself riding in a gypsy cab pulled over by the police, then being told I would have to find another way home because the driver was being arrested. Despite this, many black GIs preferred the gypsy cabbies because we trusted them; they were people of color, too.

Hansom cab drivers could be just as big a problem as the gypsies. Some would not pick up nonwhites. Among those who would pick you up, some would not turn on their meters and then try to overcharge you, too. Unlike the gypsies, the hansom cab drivers would not hesitate to involve a bobby in a fare dispute. Also, it was not uncommon for them to take you on an extended ride or engage you in a conversation designed to keep the meter running.

One evening, I took a cab from Douglas House to my home in Kensal Rise. The driver seemed pleasant enough until we got on the subject of race. When he discovered I was born in America and was not a West Indian or African, his interest seemed to pique. He asked questions about Washington, DC, my hometown. He wanted to know if I actually was born there. We talked about the States, the climate, and nearly everything else imaginable.

Then I noticed he was taking an inordinately long time to traverse what should have been no more than a twenty-minute ride. I asked him to speed up. Instead of speeding up, he talked louder and asked more questions. He complimented me on being different than most of the blacks around London, concluding, "You seem more savvy than most of the others."

Wanting to know exactly what he meant, I asked him to explain. To my surprise, he pulled over and continued to talk. I stopped him mid-sentence and suggested he turn off his meter. He did not answer, but continued to talk. I asked him again to turn off his meter, and he ignored me a second time.

This time, in the middle of his ongoing conversation, I just got out of the cab and walked the rest of the way home. I figured, why pay him to insult me by not listening to me? Later, I learned from one of the gypsy drivers that the extended conversation was one of the tricks hansom cabbies used to draw out fares. According to the gypsy driver, the cabbies would do this because they believed they could outsmart most of their customers, particularly those of color.

Bus Hopping

Most of my time in London, I was broke. The lack of money forced me to be creative not only in my eating habits, but also about transportation to work. On most days, I had the shilling or two it took to go back and forth to the office. Often, however, due to a shortage of cash, I had to resort to other means. One of those was to hop a bus, ride as far as I could, and then jump off before having to pay the fare. Two or three bus rides like that and I could get to work for free.

Double-decker buses were the best choice for this kind of free transportation. Subways or tubes were the worst. In the subway you had the problem of jumping over turnstiles, escaping the fare-takers, and, occasionally, dodging the local bobby who might be in the tube station. Rather than go through all that, it was simpler to just hop onto the open end of a double-decker bus and then hop off as the fare-taker approached.

The double-decker bus seemed designed to be used in this manner. It usually had only two people operating the bus: the fare-taker and the driver. The driver never came out of his cab. The fare-taker always seemed to start collecting funds as far from the back platform as possible. As a result, it was an easy mark for us fare-cheaters.

At first I felt guilty stealing a ride to work. Then I noticed everyone seemed to do it. Old people would hop on and off the buses as frequently or more frequently as the young. Matrons with babies did it. Men in business suits did it. And, of course, young girls in minis did it, too.

One of the funniest things I saw while in England took place during one of the free rides on a double-decker bus. It involved a young lady in an exceptionally short mini.

Stan, an army buddy, and I had just hopped on to the open end of a double-decker bus heading for Marble Arch. Getting on just behind us was a young lady who, instead of staying on the open platform with us, decided to sit on the bench seat that ran lengthwise along the back of the bus. Just as she climbed onto the seat, the bus made a rather sharp turn. This caused her to slide down the seat, pulling her mini just a little higher and exposing her crotch. Embarrassed, she tried to pull her skirt down.

As she sat there tugging at her skirt, who should come bounding down the steps from the upper level but the fare-taker. As he got to the bottom step, something shot from under the girl's skirt, hit the fare-taker in the chest, and fell to the floor, stopping him in his tracks. When he looked down, the girl made her getaway. As she jumped off the bus, we noticed her right stocking sagging slightly.

The men, including the fare-taker, began to laugh. Stan and I laughed so hard we forgot to jump off the bus behind the girl. As a result, we both had to pay the five-pence bus fare. As we paid, we looked down to see the culprit that had caused the commotion. There on the floor was one slightly frayed white garter strap. The fare-taker bent down, picked it up, and offered it to us as a souvenir, remarking, "It must be worth at least the fare you had not intended to pay."

We laughed some more, declined it, and hopped off the bus.

The Park Avenue Trotters

As I have noted, getting to work on time was sometimes a chore. Getting up was never a problem. Making the bus connections was the real issue. On most mornings, particularly in the fall and winter months, it was dark as I left the house. I had to be at the bus stop on time and clearly visible to the drivers because it was not uncommon for them to pass you by. One pass-up could cause you to miss all your connections.

On those mornings, I always had a backup plan. For me it was getting off the bus at Lancaster Gate tube station, cutting through Hyde Park, crossing Park Lane, and taking the shortcut down Green Street. This came out just in front of the North Audley Street building.

I chose this route as my shortcut because from the top of Park and Green streets I could see others entering the building, giving me an idea of how early or late I might be. Each morning between 7:35 and 7:50 a.m. the Queen's Mounted Guard rode up Park Lane and crossed Green Street on the way to the Palace for guard duty. My goal was to cross Park Lane just ahead of the Mounted Guard.

If I arrived at 7:35 a.m., I was too late. The police escort would keep you from crossing the street. Crossing the street before 7:35 a.m. put me in the office at exactly 7:45 a.m. If I got to Park Lane at 7:36 a.m. or later, I invariably would not get to the office until 8:00 a.m. Policy was to be in the office at 7:45 a.m.

Like a lot of my coworkers, I abhorred having to rush to work because, among other things, it meant that my deodorant would not usually last the entire day. So the rush to get across Park Lane had to be an act of desperation. However, on more than one occasion, I had to make that hasty trip.

One morning in particular, I got to Park Lane just as the Queen's Mounted Guard was about to complete their trip past Green Street. That morning they had finished the trip before 7:45 a.m. I believed I could still make it to work on time. Timing being everything, I figured I could make the dash across the street just behind the last police car and ahead of the rest of the traffic.

Just as the police passed, I made my move. Halfway across the street, I encountered a mound of warm, smelly horse manure. Because I was in full stride, the only thing I could do was attempt to jump over it. As I jumped, I made it across the first big pile only to land in a second smaller pile. As I landed, I lost my footing and fell square on my back in the middle of Park Lane. Unfazed, I promptly sprung to my feet and continued my dash to the office, arriving at 7:55 a.m. Although technically late, I had made it to the office before the start of the workday. As I took off my topcoat, I realized that not only had my deodorant begun to fail me, but I was also carrying the sweet aroma of horse manure on my coattail. I got permission to go back home to change clothes. By the time I returned, I was the laughing stock of the office. Word had traveled throughout the building about "Harry and the Park Avenue Trotters." Although I never saw the humor in the incident, I made it a point never to be late again.

CHAPTER THIRTEEN

Terry the Gypsy Cabbie

Without a car, getting around London late at night was not the easiest thing to do. Public transportation closed around the time pubs did; that is, around 10 p.m. during the week and 11:30 p.m. on weekends. For those with cars, this didn't present a problem. But most of us did not have cars. We were totally dependent on public transportation, the kindness of a friend, or the reliability of a minicab, a.k.a., the gypsy cab.

As I mentioned, the gypsy cab was an illegal taxi. After hours, the gypsies hung around Douglas House looking for fares. The drivers were usually dependable drivers, willing to take us anywhere in London. Unlike licensed hansom drivers, they did not mind waiting and did not charge exorbitant rates. While I was in London, I got to know a couple of the gypsy cab drivers well. Terry, a Jamaican, became a part our crowd.

I don't remember how I met Terry. However, I do know when I first met him, he struck me as what the kids today would call a *wanna be*. That is, he wanted to be an American with all his heart. He loved listening to American radio and music. As a result, he affected the banter of the American-influenced rock-and-roll disc jockeys that could be heard on the pirate radio stations like Radio Caroline and Radio Liberty. He also loved telling us how he had made a couple of trips to New York and had gone up to Harlem. So he thought he had seen America and knew what it took to be an American.

In addition to the speech, he also loved to dress like an American. He routinely wore a stocking cap and had enough Dixie Peach hair pomade in his hair to lubricate a couple of cars. He rarely wore anything other than sharkskin suits and wingtip shoes. Where he got them, we did not know. Except for the fact that his clothes always seemed to be in need of pressing, they looked pretty good. So despite his overly styled hair and his rumpled sharkskin suits, in his mind, he was just another African-American hanging out with the guys.

When I met him, Terry had been in London for nearly ten years and worked part-time at odd jobs for the merchants at Shepherd's Bush and Hammersmith Markets. As a result of his connections with the markets and his ability to finagle, he always had a ready supply of commodities for sale–cigarettes, clothes, a variety of canned goods–in the trunk of his car.

Despite the obvious, the thought of him being a black marketeer never crossed our minds. All we knew was that he was an available and willing mode of transportation that provided rides and merchandize on credit if we needed it. Between paydays, he was just another means of stretching our meager budgets. He needed the business; we needed the transportation and the commodities. We tolerated each other.

From Monday to Wednesday we rarely saw Terry. However, from Thursday evening through Saturday night he seemed to be everywhere. On Thursdays, he would be in front of Douglas House checking out our needs for him for the upcoming weekend. On Fridays, he would go to Que Club and wait for whoever might need transportation after the club closed around 2:30 a.m. On Saturday, particularly payday weekends, he could be found in front of the Navy Commissary in Earl's Court.

The Commissary was a giant supermarket located in a residential neighborhood just up from Shepherd's Bush Green. On those Saturday mornings, the Commissary was usually packed with shoppers from the American military and diplomatic communities.

Most did not have cars and would catch cabs to go
shopping. Here Terry could pick up fares and take
reservations for Saturday evenings.

On those Saturday night excursions, Terry was
punctual and dependable. However, every now and
then, we had to remind him he was the cabbie and not
one of the guys hanging out.

One time in particular occurred over the Christmas
holidays in 1967. That year, Christmas fell on a
Monday. The office party was held around the 15th.
The official obligatory staff house parties began the
following week. Then other parties, among my friends
and acquaintances, began Christmas weekend and
continued throughout Boxing Day and New Year's.

The nearly three weeks of Christmas parties took
place each of the two years I was in England for the
holidays. I must admit that while the Christmas holidays were rather depressing because I missed being
home, they were a lot of fun and made the time go
faster. It was as if Santa saved all his gifts for the
bleakest few days of the year.

During that Christmas season of 1967, we used
Terry often and included him in our party plans as if
he had become an unofficial part of the Navy staff. He
carried us to the office party, and he carried us to the
parties at people's homes. On more than one occa-

sion, he was invited in and made welcome, eating and drinking to his heart's content. He was having a good time and, rightfully, expected to get paid, too.

He had an especially good time at the office Christmas party, as we all did, because of Otis Reed, our office party Santa. The previous year, Otis had so much to drink that he passed out in the middle of the party just when he was supposed to give gifts to Command's children. It was quite a treat to watch and listen to the parents explain to their kiddies why Santa would not get up.

But this year, Otis's Santa performance was not a disappointment. The party was held at an upscale Greek restaurant in Chelsea. Because it was an adults-only party, there were no children to scandalize. Everything was going well, that is, until the restaurant's belly dancer began her performance. As she twisted and gyrated, Santa-Otis decided he could dance as well as, if not better than, she. At first, Santa imitated the dancer. Then, after a few more drinks, he began to compete. Every move the young lady made, Otis tried to outdo.

Before too long, Otis decided the best way to outdance the belly dancer was by doing his moves on a tabletop. Once on the table, he began hopping from table to table, egged on by officemates and other

restaurant patrons. Soon, he was the only person
dancing. In the midst of it all, one of the sailors placed
a couple of dollars at Otis's feet. Without missing a
beat, he reached down, scooped up the money, and
began unbuttoning his shirt.

Before long, Santa was doing a full-blown
striptease. As the music got bumpier, Santa's grinds
got wilder. It did not take long for Santa to get down
to just his beard, his boots, and his boxer shorts.
Before Otis could go further, the restaurant manager
intervened and asked all of us to leave. That was the
last year Otis played Santa. It was also the last time
our Christmas party was held outside the office.

That New Year's weekend, Terry continued to be
at our disposal. New Year's Eve he met five of us,
three guys and two girls, at Douglas House and agreed
to take us wherever we wanted to go. The girls, West
Indians, knew where the parties were so they were
essential to our plans. The fact that there were five of
us, too many for his little car, did not bother Terry. So
off we went.

First, we went out to Wembly, then back to
Harrow on the Hill. Next, we went to Earl's Court,
near the commissary, and finally ended up in Chelsea.
The total distance must have been nearly fifty miles
roundtrip. Everyone was in a good mood, but we were

not finished partying yet. The ladies knew of one more party, but as we piled into Terry's car, one of the young ladies noticed Terry seemed a bit out of it and said something to him. Before long, what had started as a question escalated into a full-blown shouting match. During the shouting, we noticed Terry had at least six empty beer bottles under his seat, all still warm with corners of beer in them, which meant they had been drunk recently.

We concluded Terry had been drinking more than we realized and probably should not be driving. When we pointed this out to him, he became very quiet. He calmly got out of the car, walked around to the passenger doors, and began to shout, "Ras mon, ya bloody Yanks, tink ya bettr'n everybody. Git 'ell outa mi car!"

We were stunned. We pleaded with him to take us back downtown. He would not. We needed him because, between the five of us, we had no more than fifteen pounds, not nearly enough to get all of us back to Douglas House in a traditional cab. We begged him, but he refused.

After nearly half an hour, who should show up but the bobbies. Some of the neighbors had heard the noise from the party and the commotion from our argument and called the cops. As they pulled up in their black Jag, a chief inspector got out. While it was not unusual for a traditional bobbie to answer such calls, it was truly rare for a chief inspector to come out. We knew we were in for some lengthy questioning, particularly if drinking and driving became an issue. In the sixties, the Brits were just beginning to learn the lessons of drinking and driving. They were really tough on those who did. And I had witnessed how they dealt with those who drove after a few drinks, particularly foreigners.

A coworker who had rear-ended a bus while intoxicated had lost his driving privileges for six months, and his *passenger* was fined for riding with someone intoxicated.

Although no one was hurt, the entire office had to attend classes on the dangers of drinking and driving, what it meant to be a guest in someone else's country, and the consequences of ignoring those driving laws.

For the individual who precipitated all of this, there was no court hearing, just a letter notifying the Command of the Crown's actions. For most of us that was lesson enough. Obviously I had not learned my lesson because there I stood in the cold in Chelsea with a drunk minicab driver.

The bobbies separated us into three groups of two each. As each group tried to explain that everything was okay, it became clear that Terry did not fit into the group. He was a little older, not American, and possibly drunk. Inevitably the cops focused on him. They told him they wanted to search the car and asked him to open the boot (trunk) of the mini.

As the police stood there lecturing us on the dangers of drinking and driving, we got a big shock. Terry had his personal liquor locker in the trunk of that little car. Not only had Terry been drinking with us at the parties, he had been drinking from the open case of beer in the trunk, too. But the case of beer was not the only thing. His trunk also contained several cases of bourbon, scotch, and vodka.

Our hearts sank. I knew we were all going to jail. As if to reinforce my fears, the police put Terry in handcuffs and placed him in the back seat of the Jag. I saw myself going home in disgrace.

The chief inspector then turned to us and asked for identification. All we had was our military ID cards. One of the girls, on the other hand, had a British driver's license. The chief inspector pulled her aside and spoke to her privately.

After a couple of minutes, he told us he was willing to forget the entire matter if we helped him with another little matter. This consisted of us removing the booze from the back of Terry's car and placing it in the gutter. After taking one bottle of evidence from each of the cases, the chief inspector had us destroy the booze. He gave us our ID cards back, called a hansom cab, released Terry, and told the young lady with the driver's license to drive Terry's car and lead the hansom cab to wherever we were going. As we got into the different cars, he said, "You Yanks shouldn't be surprised if you hear from us."

We sat in silence all the way back to Douglas House. When we arrived, the cabbie refused the fare. As he put it, he was doing his friend, the chief inspector, a favor. It was then we realized that Terry had been ripped off.

Although we were upset, we knew we sailors had dodged a big bullet. We could have been accused of bootlegging and smuggling because most of Terry's merchandise had come from the Commissary store. Of course, we never heard from the chief inspector again.

After that incident, Terry cooled towards us. He stopped being as available as he once had been. When we finally got a chance to talk to him, he swore up and down that we were bad luck. As a result, he wanted little to do with us. In hindsight, that was probably a good thing.

CHAPTER FOURTEEN

Hard Lessons

On the surface, the houses at #44 and #54 were little different than homes in the States. However, once inside, much distinguished them. Aside from the obvious differences like the pay-as-you-go gas and electric meters, there were other features most of us had not seen in America; things like paraffin and gas heaters, added-on loos (toilets attached to the rear of the house), and little or no insulation. Of these things the most dangerous were the paraffin and gas heaters.

When I first arrived in England, I met Petty Officer Roger Quentin, who had brought his family to London from the States. Within a month they had found a pleasant three-bedroom house with a large sitting room, dining room, and spacious kitchen. However, it did not have central heating. As a result, Roger and his family of three had to learn to use paraffin and gas heaters.

The gas heaters were not a problem. You turned them on, lit a match, and had a flame.

However, the paraffin heaters were another matter. First, no one told them it was necessary to clean paraffin heaters regularly. Second, no one showed them how to put the wicks in properly. And, last, no one warned them about the need for proper ventilation when using them.

The winter of 1967 in England was particularly cold and damp. It was not uncommon to go to people's homes and see them carrying paraffin heaters from one room to the other. While the British knew to crack the windows to let in air, most Americans did not. For about three days Roger had come to the office mentioning his daughter was complaining of headaches and feeling lethargic.

Then one night, they all went to bed normally. The paraffin heaters were going in both the master bedroom and the little girl's room, but none of the doors or windows were open.

Roger usually rode to work with Otis Reed (our office party Santa previously mentioned). The next morning, when Otis called to say he was on his way to pick Roger up, no one answered. Otis decided to stop and knock on the door. After knocking and knocking, Roger finally came to the door, still in nightclothes. Otis immediately smelled the fumes. He insisted that Roger check on his wife, and she, too, was difficult to awaken.

Then Otis began opening windows while Roger went to check on his daughter. He tried to wake her, but she would not respond. Although cold to the touch, she was still breathing. Immediately they called the ambulance and began opening the remaining windows and doors.

By the time the ambulance service arrived, the girl had begun turning blue. She died en route to the hospital.

The investigation into that little girl's death revealed the need to brief all incoming American personnel on the differences in British and American lifestyles. As a result of the Quentin child's death, the Command insisted we have our paraffin heaters inspected quarterly. It was a lesson I never forgot.

✦ CHAPTER FIFTEEN ✦

The Office

During my entire time in England, I worked at #7 North Audley Street, London, W1. The North Audley street address was home to the Naval Facility, England; Director, Naval Security Group; Headquarters; and the Commander In Chief, United States Naval Forces, Europe (CINCUSNAVEUR). In addition to those administrative offices, the facility also housed a post office, crypto and non-crypto communications centers, a small cafeteria, and a classified registered publications center.

For most of my tour, Admiral John S. McCain, USN, (father of Senator John McCain) was CINCUS-NAVEUR. The admiral stood no taller than five feet five inches, had a penchant for cigars ,and was a no-nonsense dynamo who seized every opportunity to instruct.

One Saturday the admiral came to the building in civilian clothes. The seaman on duty at the quarterdeck did not recognize him. As the admiral entered, the young man challenged him. Admiral McCain became irate and refused to show his credentials. To add insult to injury, he told the sailor, "You have two days to find out who I am. If you don't, I will have your ass. Do you understand me?"

Within minutes, the sailor realized who had crossed his quarterdeck. For the next couple of days, he avoided the admiral. Finally, he and Admiral McCain came face-to-face during a staff briefing. When the admiral glanced at him, the sailor was petrified. However, instead of berating him, the admiral commended him for having the chutzpah to challenge him.

Before World War II, the North Audley building had been an elegant hotel. During the War the U.S. military had moved in and converted it into the Supreme Headquarters, Allied Powers, Europe (SHAPE). Despite its military use, the building regularly revealed hints of its luxurious past. For example, one week the Director, Security Group Communications Center, approached our boss, the Commander, Security Group Europe, about reviewing the blueprints of the building to install more electronic equipment. The wall he wanted to remove may have been a load-bearing wall.

They brought in workers who took one swipe at the wall with a sledgehammer and uncovered some of the most beautiful marble they had ever seen. The workmen quickly switched to less destructive tactics. With hammers and chisels they attempted to find a seam in the marble. When they finally found the seam in a panel and removed it, behind it they found an intact men's bathroom, with functional urinals and stalls! They only had to turn on the water.

No one knew how long the room had been sealed, but to everyone's surprise, the facilities worked. So instead of an extension to the communications center, the staff wound up with a new bathroom. (Eventually a new communications center was built in a garage adjacent to the North Audley building.)

My group's office occupied the entire seventh floor of the building. The space was arranged in typical sixties military fashion: huge LGDs (large gray desks) and simple IBM typewriters. The desks were lined up in the style of the day, rows of three or four with the senior people sitting at the back and the peons at the very front. The one exception to this was the person who maintained the office files. As a seaman and the classified file clerk, I had that responsibility.

I sat in the very back of the office in front of a
bank of files covering one entire wall. All day long I
sat at that desk. On my desk sat four baskets, one each
for pink, green, and yellow carbon copies, and the
fourth for rough drafts. We maintained the files in
triplicate with each color having its own file cabinet.
Each cabinet was maintained in order of the origina-
tion date of the correspondence, with the most recent
date in front. I spent every day of my first six months
at Security Group Headquarters maintaining those
files. Initially I hated them; however, over time I
learned to like them because they saved me from a lot
of crap details.

Night School

At this point I need to digress to my pre-Navy
days. When I finished high school, obtaining my
undergraduate degree was my major focus. The entire
time I worked at the Central Intelligence Agency, I
was taking college courses at night. Initially, I did this
in an attempt to stay abreast of the guys I had graduated with from high school. But later it became a
necessity for me to advance at the CIA.

While at the agency, I worked in the Cable
Secretariat's office where we processed classified
message traffic from around the world. Physically, the

office was divided into two sections and was typical of a government office engaged in the mass production and duplication of paper documents. One section, consisting of the supervisory staff and analysts, was entirely white and engaged in thinking tasks, i.e., reading the documents, analyzing them, and determining geographically which office in the broader agency had action responsibility. The other section, all black, had responsibility for the menial tasks, i.e., duplication, collation, and distribution of the products from the other section.

I was one of six clerks who received duplicated intelligence material and then collated, stapled, and delivered it to the various offices throughout the agency's Langley, VA complex. As a recent high school graduate, I found the job interesting, particularly when I had the chance to read some of the message traffic.

Despite this obvious segregation, the office operated as if equal opportunity was the reality. Vacancies were routinely posted. All staff were encouraged to apply for those vacancies, as well as other vacancies throughout the government. We were also encouraged to take college and other courses to better ourselves. To aid individual development, the agency even had a tuition-assistance program and offered on-site courses at the office. I took advantage of both, believing I had an equal opportunity to excel. Besides, I had read some of the message traffic and really wanted to be an analyst. However, within a year of being there, I woke up to the sham of it all.

One day, I was called into my supervisor's office and presented with the opportunity to train to be a printing press operator. I had worked around the presses and knew enough about the job to know that I did not want to do that kind of work. The printing press operators were on their feet for the entire shift. Their lunch hours and time off were strictly regulated because the office had to meet prescribed deadlines for getting printed materials to the rest of the agency.

Rather than refuse the training opportunity, I asked about the chances of becoming an analyst. I was told there were no analyst positions open and, furthermore, it was unlikely any would come open in the foreseeable future. I was told the agency needed printing machine operators, and that by accepting this opportunity to work in an area where the agency needed people, I would be rewarded for my loyalty. Reluctantly, I agreed to take the training. Things began to change for me the day the training started.

That first day, I was told one of the conditions for my completing the course was for me to be available to work any shift. To do that, I was expected to drop out of my night college courses temporarily.

Two days later, I learned that the training consisted of two to three weeks of in-office tutoring; no formal schooling. A day later, I was given the last bit of information about this educational opportunity: to complete the training, I had to change my career field from general clerical to wage-board.

Wage-board programs were labor intensive: like cooking, repairing motors, warehousing, security, printing, and so forth. The general clerical programs related to office operations, administrative support, and the like.

Although the wage-board programs offered more money initially because of unscheduled overtime, opportunities for night differential, etc.; over the life of a career, those programs offered fewer opportunities for advancement, travel, and true line management positions. But what most concerned me was that the nature of the work schedule would severely restrict my ability to achieve my primary goal: getting a degree.

The thought of losing that opportunity made it easy for me to drop out of training in the middle of my second week. My supervisors were furious. For the next couple of months, they tagged me with every SLJ (shitty little job) they could find. I was assigned sole responsibility for assembling certain kinds of projects, particularly oversized, cumbersome projects.

While not an official printing machine operator, but because I had received most of the training, I was assigned as a backup for the regular operators on printing assignments. I was often forced to work overtime or face the dreaded threat of an *or else*. As a result of this change in my work environment and with the draft hanging over my head, I decided to enlist in the Navy with hopes of eventually getting back to my goal of attending college.

When I arrived in London in September 1966, I had been away from college for more than a year. I was anxious to get back in school, since within months of enlisting, I learned that college-educated military personnel (officers) made more money than enlisted men. This motivated me and besides, I had been kicking around the idea of becoming an officer.

Within weeks, I enrolled in college with the University of Maryland, London Center. I registered for three classes totaling nine semester credits, the maximum course load permitted for a night student.

My classes met on Mondays and Wednesdays (Freshman Algebra), Tuesdays and Thursdays (English

Composition), and all day Saturday (World History). In all honesty, the courses were not difficult and I really enjoyed them. Initially, the command was supportive of my going to school. However, in the spring when I wanted to take another nine semester credits, I encountered the same barriers I had met at the CIA. While the Navy wanted me to get educated, they too were more interested in their program than mine.

At the beginning of my second semester, but before registration for classes, I was approached by the executive officer (XO) regarding the staff's need for someone to help out by running one of the office printing presses located in the classified communications center.

As he put it, the office had a billet for a printing machine specialist but was being denied one by Washington. Furthermore, he continued, I had a Top Secret clearance and access to the communications center and could really help the command by volunteering to fill the printing press billet until Washington saw fit to send someone. Besides, he added, his favorable comments about my volunteering could help me get promoted.

Reluctantly, I agreed with the understanding that I could continue to take classes. That semester I took only two classes: European History and Speech and Writing.

Within days of this agreement, I found myself in European History engaged in a heated debate regarding colonialism and the particular benefits slavery had bestowed upon blacks generally, and me specifically. The person articulating my benefits was a senior enlisted man, Bob Kurzinsky, who also happened to be one of my office supervisors. As he put it, all I had to do was compare my living standard to the rest of the world's black people. To him, slavery gave us black people an opportunity to become educated and civilized!

Besides, he continued, I had been offered the opportunity to run the office printing machines because it afforded me an opportunity to work with my hands and not have to worry about the more difficult tasks of composing correspondence, setting filing systems, and learning policy and procedure manuals.

Finally, he concluded, it was a known fact that blacks preferred working with their hands rather than their heads!

I was flabbergasted. It took all the self-control I could muster to keep from going into a rage.

The next morning, I was sitting outside the XO's office when he came in. I told him about the conversation from the class and asked out of the agreement. He agreed to forget the agreement, all the while reassuring me that Kurzinsky was wrong. I later learned that Kurzinsky received a royal butt-chewing as a result of his asinine remarks.

While this event left a bitter taste in my mouth, it proved to be rather fortuitous. Unbeknownst to me, at the time I was volunteering my time working on the printing presses, the white sailors within my unit were forming special tutorial sessions to prepare them for upcoming advancement exams. As though to show me how wrong Kurzinsky had been, the XO made it a point to let me know about the classes and ordered one of the other supervisors to tutor me personally, thereby ensuring I passed. Although I was appreciative of this gesture, the entire affair made me even more determined to finish college.

Marines and the Ice Cream Cone!

Another office duty while stationed at the North Audley building was to pick up the classified message traffic from the communications center serving the non-Security Group occupants of the building. I would usually do this first thing in the morning and last thing in the afternoon. Following the afternoon pickup, around 3:30 p.m., I would often cut through the main hallway on my way back to the office or go to the Ice Cream Parlor in the basement. At the same time, the Marines were usually lining up in formation for the changing of the guard.

It was impressive to watch the changing of the guard because the Marines were the only U.S. military personnel in London who still maintained some semblance of pomp and pageantry. Most of them were guys who had reenlisted for duty in London after serving in Vietnam. Of those who fit this category, most usually came straight from the jungles of Southeast Asia to London, with no stop in the States. As a result, some of them had been out of the combat zone less than a month. The hardening jungle experience made them more serious in their military bearing. This all contributed to a rather impressive ten-minute ceremony.

Captain Skinner, my commanding officer, loved ice cream. Some afternoons he would ask me to pick up some as I did my mail run. That afternoon, I stopped for his cone and had gotten a scoop for myself. I was in a hurry because I had also decided to stop and watch the changing of the guard.

As I indicated, the North Audley building was full of old marble, so the slightest sounds had a tendency to reverberate. That afternoon, as I walked through

the hallway watching the Marines begin their ceremony, which included checking their weapons to
ensure no rounds remained in the chamber, things
went terribly wrong. Properly checking a Colt .45
pistol includes pulling the trigger *after* ensuring an
empty chamber. If done correctly, all you should get is
a click. That day, one of the Marines had not done it
correctly. Instead of a click, he got the exaggerated
retort of his weapon discharging in a marble hallway.

Suddenly I found myself in the middle of a bunch
of Marines, recently arrived from Vietnam, locking,
loading, and pointing their weapons *at me.* It took the
Sergeant of the Guard a considerable amount of time
to get the Marines settled down.

I lost my taste for afternoon ice cream cones that
day. And I had a helluva time explaining to the
captain why I no longer cared for those late afternoon
trips downstairs.

The Dirt Rearrangers

Among other duties were a series of little crap
details. One of the worst was cleaning the office, which
we did weekly. The building's general maintenance
people were not allowed into our work area because
we handled classified materials. To enter our office
spaces, you had to pass through a bolted door with

sliding windows for identification checks and then through another door with a series of cipher locks. With that kind of security and the cost of doing background checks on all those who had access to the space, the Navy decided it was cheaper to have the staff (meaning the junior enlisted) do the cleaning rather than spend the money on clearances for outsiders.

On those days when we cleaned the office, we brought our dungarees to work but wore them all day anyway because little else got done. We would pick up our mops, brooms, and vacuum cleaners, and, with the noise and dust, run everyone out of their workspaces. Although we called it cleaning, our efforts usually consisted of spreading old dirty water on even dirtier floors, then adding new wax to old.

During my two years in London, I don't remember us ever getting new mops or changing the water once we got started. While we considered it okay to add clean water to the dirty, changing the water was strictly forbidden. You see, changing the water might have actually cleaned a spot. And had that clean spot been noticed by higher-ups, it could have necessitated the need to actually clean the office. None of us wanted that.

Although cleaning was a break in the routine, I did not like it because the work usually got me so dirty that it meant I had to go straight home after work to clean myself up. This, of course, limited my time at Douglas House. Early on, I sought ways to get out of the cleaning details. One way was to let the office files pile up.

Coffee, Mates!

Another task I had as one of the junior people in the office was to make morning coffee. Our official workday was from 8:00 a.m. to 4:00 p.m. However, to make the coffee, I had to be in the office at least a half hour before everyone else. Getting in earlier also meant turning off the alarms, turning on the lights, walking through the spaces, and checking to see if things were as we had left them the night before.

Ordinarily, making coffee is simple. However, the size of our pot presented a problem. Our office consisted of approximately forty people and, on average, each person drank three cups of coffee each morning. We used a one-hundred-fifty-cup pot. To fill this meant carrying the pot to the deep sink, emptying the contents, then bringing it back full of water. We usually spilled water or coffee everywhere.

To make the trip less precarious, we decided rather than carry all that water and coffee back and forth, we should have a two-pot system. Originally, we decided to keep one pot brewing and the other on standby. However, over time, the two-pot system evolved into a brewing pot and a sludge pot. The brewing pot usually contained fresh water and grounds. The other became the repository for all the used grounds, dregs, and sludge from the day or, most often, the days before.

In theory, we would empty the sludge daily, too. However, in time, we only emptied as it filled up, usually at the end of the week.

This system came to an end the day the XO, Commander March, arrived at the office earlier than anyone else. Wanting a cup of coffee but not wanting to go down to the basement cafeteria, he decided to plug in one of the coffee pots. He inadvertently plugged in the sludge pot.

When I came in, I immediately noticed the sludge pot had brewed and the fresh pot was still off. I checked with a few of the other sailors to ensure no one had drunk from the sludge pot. It was too late. The commander had consumed not one, but two cups of coffee. Rather than tell him, I quietly brewed a fresh pot of coffee, turned off the sludge pot, and hoped for the best.

That afternoon, the commander went to the dispensary complaining of stomachaches and diar- rhea. The other sailors and I sat in stunned silence, knowing but not knowing what he was up against.

Later that day, as we emptied the pot, we finally saw what had accumulated at the bottom. Not only were there baked-in grounds, but also what appeared to be a variety of fungi, slimes, and what once could have been roaches.

For two days, he was at home, sick in bed. When he finally came back to work, he was livid. The doctors had run tests and concluded he had ingested something that made him very ill. Then he told us that, before going to the doctor, he had taken a look into the pot and saw what he had been drinking. He ordered us to get rid of the sludge pot and threatened to court-martial us for attempted murder if he ever saw a second pot again.

It took us awhile to face him after that, but eventually we did; to our surprise, he even learned to laugh at the sludge pot ordeal.

The Classifieds

Another crap detail was taking the classified trash to the incinerator. The incinerator was at one of the municipal trash sites across the Thames in East Putney. Those of us who were cleared to handle sensitive information would take turns. Going to the incinerator was a dirty job and involved traveling to one of the toughest neighborhoods in London. On those trips, you had to watch the trash as well as your back. It was not uncommon for some bloke on the streets to toss something at you as you rode by on the back of the open truck. Or, worse yet, at the incinerator, as a joke, one of them might hand you a bag of bottles, which tended to explode in the heat of the fire.

The worst thing that happened to me on one of those details was losing a bag of classified trash, which fell unnoticed off the back of the truck. We discovered it was missing when we arrived at the incinerator, since each bag was numbered and we were one bag short.

We called the office. They in turn called both military security and British Intelligence. Losing classified trash was considered a major breach of security, and it prompted an immediate full-scale search.

To find the trash, we had to walk the entire four-mile route back to the office. During the first sweep, we found nothing. On the second trip, one of the guys found the bag under a parked lorry. Although the bag appeared intact, it was placed in the back of one of the military police sedans and whisked away to the office to verify its contents.

This involved checking the number of the bag, calling the office of origin, and finally opening the bag in the presence of someone from that office. We did all that. But when the bag was opened, it did not contain classified trash; instead, it was full of old potato chip bags, soda cans, and paper cups! This was a violation of security.

I was mad. I had walked all that distance for a bag of ordinary trash. As a result of that incident, the office established new protocols for handling classified trash. Offices with classified trash to be burned had to assign someone to bring the trash down to the loading dock. On the loading dock, the person from the cognizant office went through each of his bags with the men escorting them to the incinerator. Once they were verified to have classified trash only, the escorts signed for the bags and assigned them numbers.

Because I was on the detail that lost the first bag, I was given the task of being one of the first to implement these new protocols. What a waste of time!

Chauffeur Duty?

Although I had a driver's license, I never drove while stationed in England. However, that did not stop the Navy from ordering me to take the Navy road test to get my duty driver's license. All of the staff seamen were assigned to be duty drivers. It was expected that we would chauffeur the admirals, captains, and other visiting dignitaries to meetings, the airport, and other bases as part of our military duties.

The day of my test, I told the Brit administering the test that I had not driven much and was uncertain about driving on "the wrong side of the road." Unperturbed, he insisted that I take the wheel. We drove from North Audley Street up to Baker Street and over to St. John's Woods, near the Marine barracks. Things were going fine until he told me to turn without advance warning. Instead of turning just then, I kept going straight for approximately another twenty feet and hit the front gate at the entrance to the park. The car was a total wreck.

That ended my driving days in England. While I was the laughing stock of the office, some began to think I crashed the car deliberately because the accident knocked me off the duty driver roster.

✧ CHAPTER SIXTEEN ✧

The Sporting Life

When not at Douglas House, we spent a great deal of our off-duty time either attending or participating in sporting events. These diversions included boxing matches, attempting to play golf, going to dog races, occasional horseback-riding, watching or playing American football, and watching or playing soccer or rugby.

I learned early on that it was safer to be a spectator, particularly with soccer and rugby. While in England, rugby was the game that I most enjoyed and attempted to play. The fun in rugby was that it appealed to the ego. The guys were bloody and rolling around in the mud. They drank beer between scrums and, because of the constant kicking and running, you felt you were really competing in a true *manly* sporting activity. This was not like soccer or American football where you actually needed a strategy to win. In rugby, brute power won the matches.

I played rugby with some of the guys in the office for most of my first four months in England. However, my playing came to an end the weekend we literally got our butts kicked.

That morning, a group of us met at the North Audley building and drove out to Rislip Air Force Base for what was to have been our final match. Rislip is about fifty minutes from downtown. We were rather worked up by the time we arrived at the base.

As a team, we were a mediocre lot. Going into the game, we had a record of four wins and ten losses. But we clung to hopes of winning. The team we were to play had an even worse record (two wins/eight losses). However, judging by the way they played and our final score, you would not have believed they were that bad.

Our team played in an informal league. We rarely had fifteen players for a full team. As a result, we often played without substitutions. Our team was made up of American sailors who had learned the game while in England. For us, the object of the game was to have fun, occasionally beat other American teams, and drink lots of beer.

When we arrived at Rislip, we thought we were playing airmen from the base. As servicemen playing in an all-American league, we should have known most of our opponents because each team played the other at least twice during the season. However, that day, we only recognized a handful. It really didn't matter because we had come to have fun and to kick some Air Force butt! Just before the game began, we were told we would be playing a replacement team because the original opponents were on alert for base war games.

Things went downhill from the opening whistle. During the first scrum, they managed to bowl us over and score with little resistance. During subsequent play and before the second scrum, we came up with a strategy to foul them without getting penalized. That strategy worked perfectly until they began to drop-kick the ball. As a result of their kicking and passing, by the time the first half ended, they had scored twenty points to our zero. Then they stopped fooling around and decided to get physical.

The scrums became huddles for beating the hell out of us. Before long, each one of our players had been either punched or poked in the jaw, eye, or stomach. It got so bad that, due to our injuries and without replacement players, we were literally playing blind. Trying to salvage some dignity from imminent defeat, we tried to forfeit but the refs would not let us.

Mercifully, after what seemed to be a lot longer than eighty minutes (the time it takes to play a rugby match), the game ended with a score of twenty-eight to three. No one was in a festive mood, with the score so lopsided, but we decided to stop at the base club for a beer or two to salve our wounds.

In the club were some of the spectators who had watched the debacle. A few were laughing and joking about how the airmen had managed to stomp the shit out of those swaggering-ass sailors from North Audley. At first we ignored them, but then, they let the cat out of the bag. One airman, who obviously did not recognize us, shouted, "The sailors were too damned dumb to know they were playing against some of the guys from the U.S. Air Force German rugby championship team!"

We had been suckered!

For the rest of the afternoon, we went from office to office at Rislip until we found one of the guys who had officiated at our game. When we explained to him what had happened, he was able to get the game declared a win for us. As we left the base, we felt smug because once again, the sailors had managed to outwit the airmen and beat them at their game and on their turf. On our way off the base, we stopped at the club to have one last beer. How sweet it was watching as our opponents heard of their defeat. It made our day, watching the champs turn out to be chumps for trying to steal the game. With that, my rugby days ended.

After rugby, I began to get into the horse races. In England, off-track betting is a lively business, and I learned to enjoy it. On a daily basis, I would go to the City Tote (a betting shop) to check on the horse races. The atmosphere at the tote shop was lively. There was plenty of beer, a lot of joshing, and the lure of winning big.

To play, you could bet on a horse to win, place, or show. I usually bet to show because the odds of winning were greater. Around the time my brother-in-law was killed, I had become a frequent bettor at City Tote, betting on the dogs, the horses, and the prize fights.

As winter moved into spring, City Tote began showing odds on the running of the Grand National, one of the biggest horse meets of the year. The race is run in April at Aintree in Liverpool. Horses must race around a four-and-a-half mile track that's been called one of the most challenging and dangerous fields in England. The race is essentially a steeplechase with horses required to jump hedgerows, water traps, and other obstacles. Over the years the jumps have been modified to reduce the risk of danger or death to both the riders and the horses. Despite this, the race has more than its share of spills and falls which, when you throw in a wager, makes the race even more exciting.

For about a month (before going home for my brother-in-law's funeral), a bunch of us had been placing our change in a cigar box in anticipation of the race. The plan was to pool our resources and place a bet on each of the favorites *and* on the longest shot in the Grand National. That year we had all of the horses covered, or so I thought.

While home, I got the results of the race from the *Washington Daily News*. The horse that won was a 100-1 long shot by the name of Foinavon. I just knew we had won a lot of money. When I got back to England, I wasted no time calling the office to see how much money our little pool had won. To my surprise, we had won only £50.

As it turned out, in my absence, the other members of the pool had decided to not place much money on the long shot. Instead, they placed most of the money on a group of four horses, all with much more favorable odds. At first I did not mind. But then I learned the person who had come up with the idea to place the bets on the four favorites had won £300 betting on the horse that won.

I was so livid that I took the matter to the commanding officer. Despite my complaint, he decided not to intervene because, according to him, "You guys should not have been betting anyway."

I learned my lesson. From then on, I never got involved in another pool, instead placing my own bets at City Tote. Despite never making a killing like the bet that yielded the £300, I did manage to more than break even before I left London.

✧ CHAPTER SEVENTEEN ✧

An American Sailor in Paris

As mentioned, Europe had long been on my short list of places to go. When I got to London, I was very excited because I knew I was realizing my dream. During the mid-sixties, many Americans still viewed Europe as a faraway place that most would never see.

I wasted no time formulating plans to see as much of Europe as I could. Many Americans stationed in London could not overcome that psychological barrier of the distance between America and Europe, and thus did not venture onto the continent. I was one of the few who took trips to France, Spain, and Italy.

Of those who did venture out, nearly all returned with stories about the various deficiencies of the continent. The stories usually centered around such things as the lack of spoken and written English, no

American-style sanitation, no American food, and, worst of all, people drove on the wrong side of the road. The stories would often conclude with some kind of bad ending: "I could not find a bathroom, so I had to urinate behind a tree in public;" or "I ordered what I thought was a steak and it turned out to be horsemeat;" or "I had an accident because the guy overtook me on the right." Stories such as these inhibited some from traveling to the continent, but they didn't stop me.

Before my first trip to France, one of the worst stories I heard involved an office mate, Roger Hoover. Roger had decided to take his wife to Paris for a weekend of fun. Throughout their preparations for the trip, several of the sailors provided opinions about the lousy French food and the poor driving habits of "Pierre" (their name for all Frenchmen). The day before they left, some even opined, "No decent man would take a woman, let alone his wife, to Paris, the sex capital of the free world." Despite the ribbing and the warnings, Roger and his wife Evelyn took off on their getaway.

The trip was an all-inclusive weekend. All went well until Saturday evening. Roger and Evelyn decided to break away from the planned activities and do the town on their own. One of the places they both wanted to see was Pigalle, known throughout the world for its open prostitution.

The Pigalle, or pig alley as the sailors called it, had block after block of scantily-clad ladies of the evening sitting in picture windows soliciting clients. It also had a reputation for robberies and other crimes.

Despite this, the tour materials touted it as a place to be seen. Even so, few people ventured there on their own. For safety reasons, most went on guided tours.

Roger and Evelyn did not think much about it. They took off on their own in search of the infamous Pigalle, and with little effort found their way to the area.

They were walking along lazily, taking in the sights, just enjoying each other's company. Then, for a brief moment, the two were separated by just a couple of yards. When Roger noticed this, he tried to catch up with Evelyn but found his way blocked by an attractive woman.

As he moved to go around her, she stepped in front of him and asked, "Are you an American?"

To which Roger answered, "Yes, I am. Why?"

She replied, "Are you looking to have a good time?"

But no sooner had she asked the question when Evelyn, hearing the conversation, turned and responded for Roger, "No, he is not. He is with me!"

The woman glared at Evelyn. Barely acknowl-
edging her, the woman placed one hand on her hip,
the other on her blouse, and while stroking her breasts,
looked straight at Roger and said in perfect English, "I
don't see why you would want to be with her. After all,
she has no shape and my breasts are larger than hers.
Besides, I know I can beat any price she offers!"

Evelyn was aghast and hurt. Hastily, she turned
and walked away, leaving Roger standing there with
the woman. For a split second, Roger did not know
what to do. He said nothing and was in such a state of
shock that he hardly noticed Evelyn leaving.

Coming to his senses, he moved past the woman
and hurried to catch Evelyn, but it was too late. She was
crying and shouting at Roger, "Can you believe that
woman would make such remarks to me, your wife?"

Before Roger could answer, Evelyn frowned at him
and continued, "And, Roger, you just stood there and
let her say those awful things to me. How could you?"

Roger was dumbfounded. Realizing he was in a
no-win situation, he decided to keep his mouth shut.
Evelyn continued to cry. They caught a cab and
returned to the hotel in silence. That one event in
Pigalle ruined an otherwise enjoyable trip and
would become the subject of derisive conversation
back in London.

Early the next morning, Roger and Evelyn left for London ahead of the rest of the group. All Evelyn wanted was to get home and forget about Paris, Pigalle, and the prostitute. But the story did not die there. Others who worked at the North Audley building had accompanied them on the trip. Some of them had learned of the incident from the concierge at the Paris hotel.

By the next morning, Monday, the story was all over the building. When I stopped in the office cafeteria for an egg sandwich, I heard others talking about how a Parisian prostitute had insulted some guy's wife.

I laughed about it, until I got to the office. When I walked in, Don Betts was in a heated argument with Roger. Apparently, Don had decided to spread the story without knowing that Roger and Evelyn had been the parties involved. Don had gotten the story wrong. In his version, the guy's wife had found her husband in a compromising position with the prostitute.

To nip the rumor in the bud, Roger decided to tell the whole story. Once he finished, he asked us not to repeat it because it had distressed Evelyn so. Everyone agreed.

But just as Roger walked away, Don decided he had to have the final say. He shouted, "Hey Roger, I guess you learned your lesson?"

"Which lesson?"

"Next time you will know better than to take a ham sandwich to a banquet."

We could not believe our ears. I thought, "How could he be so crass?"

But Roger, turning around, just shook his head, smiled sheepishly and said, "You can bet your sweet ass on that one!" We all laughed. The incident was never mentioned again.

CHAPTER EIGHTEEN

Vampire Liberty

We spent a great deal of time in England consuming alcohol. We drank British lager, stout, ales, American beer, rum, bourbon, scotch, vodka, and most anything liquid that contained alcohol. However, we did not do drugs. Who needed drugs with alcohol in such plentiful supply and so cheap to get? Although it was already inexpensive and readily available, we continually sought ways to further decrease the price while increasing its intensity.

Early on, I learned the value of being an active member of the Royal Red Cross Society. Once every six weeks, the Royal Red Cross Society would come to the building for donations of money and blood. Few gave money. Many gave blood.

To give blood, you had to make an appointment. No appointment, no donation. The sailors were particularly diligent in performing this charitable act.

Oddly though, they insisted on having appointments in the early afternoon. When I first arrived in London, I thought giving blood was part of some Navy tradition. It did not take long to find out otherwise.

Douglas House opened its doors for business at 3:30 p.m. Happy hour started at 4:00. On donation days, most sailors would give blood between 1:30 and 3:00. That gave them enough time to give blood, get the sugary drink the Brits passed off as orange juice into their system, then make it to the club for first call of happy hour.

As indicated earlier, drinks were two for the price of one during happy hour. So, with a pint less blood in your body, a really diligent drinker could effectively get double the impact at half the price. As far as we were concerned, there was no better way to save money on alcohol and perform a public service, too.

However, once the Navy learned of this practice, they made it known they did not approve of that kind of community service. As a matter of fact, they put an end to it after a couple of servicemen passed out and nearly died from acute alcohol poisoning. The joint services put out a notice that practitioners of this form of community service would be subject to court-martial.

Interestingly, the threat of a court-martial carried more weight than the possibility of death. Everyone knew someone who had died in Vietnam, so death meant little. But no one wanted to be court-martialed. In less than six months the practice disappeared, and, I was told, blood donations to the Royal Red Cross Society dropped by half.

CHAPTER NINETEEN

The Bros

Life in London might have been boring had it not been for the loose-knit group of friends whom I came to call the Bros, short for the brothers. Although most were African-Americans, they included a mixture of people from diverse racial and ethnic groups, both guys and girls. They became my family while I was in England.

At times we numbered as many as fifteen, but the core group consisted of seven people. They were: John Williams, whom you met earlier, Ted Jones, Alfredo Dean, Fitz Clark, William Kip, Stan Ervin, and myself.

Ted

Ted Jones and I became roommates after John went to live with his future wife Irene. Compared to John, Ted was quite settled. He was approximately four years older than I, making him nearly eight years older than John. Ted was a meticulous roommate, very responsible, and much more mature than the rest of us. When he and I first became roommates, I thought of him as an older brother. That was fine until he began trying to tell me what to do.

According to him, the other sailors and I were much too playful; we did not appreciate that we were stationed in London and not living as real military people. And worse yet, according to him, we were immature little boys who had no respect for the ladies we dated. In his words, "You guys treat women as if they're objects." He insisted we should be more like him: mature, understanding of women, appreciative, and focused on our careers. His preaching might have worked had we not begun to examine the truth of his life. In reality, Ted came close, but was not quite what he wanted us to be.

After awhile I found that he was set in his ways, highly opinionated, and he rarely got along with anyone, least of all women. Like the rest of us, he never seemed to be able to keep a girlfriend. Although he made more money than we did, he, too, always seemed to be short on cash. And when it came to the Navy, although he had been in the service for nearly four years when I met him, he did not know whether he was going to make it a career. So much for his preaching, and I began to doubt all the big brother/mentor crap, too. Despite this, he and I did get along, and I learned to like his company.

Ted moved in after he and a lady friend, Gloria, had just broken up. According to him, they were basically incompatible. She wanted to party; he wanted to watch the telly and just enjoy her company. Neither would give in.

This was fortuitous for me because I was glad to have his help getting the place in shape. And once we got it cleaned, he also helped keep it that way. With Ted living there, we kept plenty of food, beer, and liquor around. I must admit, the house did seem more like a home.

Despite his good intentions, Ted would often do things that reminded me *too much* of home. Although I reached the point where I did not mind his constant cautions about partying and meeting women, other things began to bug me. He would pick up my dirty laundry, offer to shine my shoes when he was doing his, and always made sure I had clean, pressed dress shirts for work. He even went so far as to dig my uniforms out of the bottom of the closet and get them dry-cleaned without my knowing it.

But the final straw involved Douglas House. He never wanted to go to the club. He preferred to stay home and cook because, according to him, it was smarter to stay home rather than go to the club and waste time and money. Of course, that fell on deaf ears. Eventually, I resigned myself to the fact that I had a roomie with some funny habits.

One week, Ted and I were both out of the flat for a couple of days. The week before, he and I had gone to the Commissary and purchased a lot of groceries, including a chuck roast of beef, eggs, bacon, and other perishables. The roast weighed three pounds. We had planned to eat it for Sunday dinner.

As things unfolded, the electricity went off. The roast, the eggs, and the other perishables sat warm in the fridge for two days. Needless to say, when we returned, everything was going bad. The meat had begun to smell and was turning green. The eggs had rotted. The rest of the perishables had to be thrown out, too. However, Ted insisted he could salvage the meat. I told him not to bother, but he ignored me.

First, he soaked the meat in salt water. Then, he marinated it in vinegar. Next, he put meat tenderizer on it and pulverized it with a meat mallet. Finally, he scraped away any remaining green. Then he proceeded to bake it with potatoes, garlic, onions, and other seasonings. I must admit the meat smelled great while it was cooking. But I could not forget its having been green and smelly. When it came time to eat, I refused the roast.

Ted had a fit. He accused me of not trusting him. He cursed me and added, "Your picky attitude will keep you away from some really great opportunities in life."

I laughed and said, "I'm sorry, but I don't see eating this roast as one of those great opportunities. Besides," I concluded, "only someone foolish would eat *poisoned meat.*"

The words *poisoned meat* infuriated him. He pushed me aside and yelled, "Screw you!" Then he sat down and ate the entire roast. Out of guilt, I ate a few of the potatoes. However, within the hour, I was proved right.

First, Ted complained of severe stomachaches. Then he began to sweat profusely. I offered to call a cab to take him to the hospital. He refused. Then he got one of the worst cases of diarrhea I have ever seen. For the better part of three hours, he was in and out of the bathroom. He took Pepto-Bismol, then drank milk. Nothing helped. Finally, almost five hours later, it began to let up. It's a good thing the diarrhea did let up because I didn't. I never let him forget the *poisoned meat* episode.

The next day at work, I made it a point to tell the guys. Soon they were spreading the word. Before long, everyone in the building knew about the bad roast and Ted's marathon diarrhea. Ted never forgave me for that. But eventually, the story of the roast became more of a joke than a source of irritation.

Six months after we became roommates, Ted received orders to Scotland. Although he and I parted friends, we did later lose contact. From the time we left England, I always seemed to be chasing him. Sometimes I would catch up with him by phone, but more often than not, I missed him.

When he and I last spoke, we joked about the *poisoned meat*. That conversation took place in 1984. By then, Ted had become a chief petty officer and was preparing to retire; I had been back on active for almost ten years and was a lieutenant. We laughed at the prospect of us having ascended to the leadership ranks of the Navy.

In 1986, I was transferred to Washington, DC to work on the staff of the Chief of Information in the Plans and Policy Section. My duties at that time included reviewing old messages and culling them for items of interest that others might have missed. Among the messages were active duty death notifications.

Generally, I skimmed those because they rarely had any value. One particular morning, I read two death notifications. The second was a copy of Ted's, addressed to his family in Washington, DC.

Ted had always been overweight and a diabetic. The disease had begun to manifest itself while we were in England. However, he did little about it. That morning, I learned the disease had finally caught up with Ted. He had died two weeks before at the age of forty-four. I combed the back copies of the local newspaper looking for his funeral, and I finally found it in a two-day-old paper.

Ted's funeral had been just the day before I saw the initial message. Chief Petty Officer Ted Jones, USN, had been buried the previous morning at Arlington National Cemetery with full military honors. I cursed, angry with myself for having once again missed Ted. Then I cried, said a prayer for my dear friend, and informed the rest of the guys with whom I was still in touch. In hindsight, I feel honored to have been the one to have discovered Ted's death notice. It seems to say that even at his death, Ted and I still had a connection that had lasted all those years.

The Road Rager

Of all of the guys I met while stationed in London, Petty Officer Third Class Alfredo Dean was the most puzzling. One of the brightest people I have ever known, he was a good guy and a genuine friend. I regret not keeping in touch with him.

In 1966, Dean, a radioman, had just completed a tour in Vietnam. He reenlisted so he could come to England to focus on getting promoted before returning to the fleet. I was impressed by his motivation to succeed. Unlike the rest of us, he was one of the few people who kept a steady girlfriend nearly the entire time we were in London. Her name was Marcia.

Marcia, a very attractive Jamaican, worked in one of the offices in central London and made good money. This was evident because, unlike most of the women we knew, Marcia did not live in a room or with her parents. Instead, she had her own flat. In addition, she was well spoken, confident, and was obviously an educated and sophisticated lady. Although she considered herself a Jamaican, she had grown up in London and received most of her education there. When she and Dean would come to Douglas House, she was always impeccably dressed.

During his tour in Vietnam, Dean had several fancy lace shirts custom-made. Those shirts and Marcia's suits and stylish manner made them the envy of many who frequented the club. This seemed to please Dean to no end. Despite this, he routinely took her for granted. This, combined with his excessive drinking and bad habits, drove Marcia up the wall. None of us understood why he sometimes acted this way, because he appeared to have what we all wanted: an attractive, attentive, articulate, and sophisticated lady friend.

Throughout their near-two-year relationship, Marcia tried her best to help Dean control his drinking. However, sometimes she was not around and he would get totally out of control. On one occasion, he got into a chugging contest with several guys he knew from Vietnam. They had drunk more than twelve beers when they decided to progress to depth charges. A depth charge is a mug of beer with a shot of bourbon dropped into it, shot glass and all!

After nearly two hours of this, Marcia showed up at the club looking for Dean. One of the guys signed her in. Before Dean knew it, she was standing behind him fuming. Rather than make a scene, Marcia just walked up to him and softly whispered in his ear, "Thank you for the lovely evening." Shocked, he turned around just as she walked away. He had forgotten their plans to meet in the dining room for dinner. Like a lost little boy, Dean got up, paid his share of the tab, then went looking for her. I don't know what she said to him, but from then on, when Dean was to meet her at the club, he assiduously avoided the bar. Instead, he waited for her at the front door of the club.

Dean spent a great deal of his time with another sailor named Hastie. The two had been stationed together in Vietnam and loved recapping their exploits. These recappings led to their joint involvement in dangerous, or just plain stupid things. One of their more outrageous episodes took place one morning on the way home from the office, after a midnight-to-eight radio-room shift.

At 8:30 that particular morning, the two of them decided to have a beer. As they headed home in Dean's Triumph, together they consumed a six-pack of beer. Almost home, Dean entered a roundabout without paying much attention to the traffic and rear-ended someone in the circle. The driver, an Englishman on his way to work, jumped out and, without looking at his car, called Dean a nigger. Dean calmly climbed out of the Triumph, open beer in hand, then cold-cocked the guy, laying him out.

Without missing a beat, he finished his beer, threw the can down at the man's feet, climbed back into his car, and drove away.

The office found out about the incident because several witnesses recognized Dean as an American. Assuming the provocateur was a serviceman, British authorities contacted the American naval offices on North Audley Street. Within two days, the Navy had gathered the handful of blacks on staff and asked us to assist the investigation. Assisting usually meant your being questioned by British police until they determined you had nothing to do with the particular incident. At the end of the investigation, the British had captured the culprits. However, instead of taking Dean in for charges, the British decided to allow the American authorities to handle the entire matter. Dean was to go before the captain for non-judicial punishment (NJP).

Initially, we thought Dean had gotten off light. Under British law, he would have lost his driving privileges and been fined. However, when Dean went before the captain for the NJP, he received a much more severe punishment. He was forced to apologize verbally to the British driver, fined $100, had to pay to have the man's car inspected to determine if there had been any damage, and he was banned from Douglas House for 30 days.

The captain explained to Dean that he was given such punishment because, "You have to remember you are a guest in their country."

Dean was upset. He later learned that once the British determined there had been a racial epithet used, they wanted nothing to do with the entire matter. However, the Americans wanted to make a point about drinking and driving, so they decided to impose the severe punishment.

Ironically, it was Hastie's testimony about the racial remark that convinced the British not to pursue the matter. Despite Hastie's involvement, the Navy decided not to punish him. Then, as if to add insult to injury, Hastie mentioned the incident to Marcia, which precipitated an argument between Marcia and Dean. Marcia ended their relationship, and Dean's drinking intensified. Last I heard, Dean had requested orders back to Southeast Asia. He had had enough of London.

Fitz

Fitz Clark was a radioman who worked with me in the North Audley facility. From the moment he and I met, we became friends. At that time we were both looking for a place to stay, so we agreed to be roommates.

Earlier, I recounted my racially tinged departure from the Stokes' place in Kilburn. Although I was surprised by the incident, I should not have been because I had already encountered other examples of British racism while searching for an apartment. However, my upbringing in the States did little to prepare me for what I saw in London.

Often, despite my American accent, I was treated differently. I was black, so a lot of British shops, apartments, and pubs wanted nothing to do with me. Still, we found ways to use our American-ness as a means of getting around the bigotry. Sometimes it worked; sometimes it did not. Other times, it led to rather humorous situations. One occasion occurred when Fitz and I were looking for an apartment.

As a radioman, he worked shift work and had days off, which made it convenient when looking for an apartment. We worked out a deal where I would scour the papers in the evenings for flats, then he would go look at them during the day. One day I found what appeared to be a really neat flat near the office. It was fully furnished, and best of all, it had two bedrooms, a private kitchen, and bath. I called, identified myself as an American, and made arrangements for my roommate to go around to take a look. The English lady who answered the phone was pleased at the prospects of renting to a couple of Americans. So I sent Fitz around.

Fitz grew up in New York City but was born in the Virgin Islands. He was dark skinned and at the time, had a thick West Indian accent. All of this meant little to me. He arrived at the flat within a half hour of my call. When he knocked on the door and asked about the flat, the woman told him there was nothing available.

Dejected, Fitz called me wanting to know why I'd sent him on a wild goose chase. I told him I hadn't and sent him back a second time. This time when he knocked on the door, the woman not only told him there was nothing available but also threatened to call the police.

So Fitz called me back a second time and asked me to call the woman on the other line to find out what was going on. I put the phone down and called the woman on another phone.

As soon as she heard my voice, she asked excitedly, "Mr. Butler, when are you coming to see the flat?" Before I could tell her that I had sent my prospective roommate around, she blurted out, "I wish you would hurry and come. There's a blackie who has been inquiring about the flat, too.

"But," she continued, "you needn't worry, I can assure you I will never rent to him or anyone like him."

Then the light went on in my head. She thinks I am white because of my accent! I responded, "Can you hold for a second?"

I placed her on permanent hold, went back to Fitz, and told him what was going on. Eventually she hung up. Fitz and I had a good laugh and forgot about the flat. Later, years later, we reminisced about how naïve we had been.

Back in Washington, DC, I had been sheltered from overt racism. I remember seeing and hearing the stories of lynchings, cross burnings, and other racial incidents. But those things happened in faraway places like Mississippi, North Carolina, Georgia, Alabama, and elsewhere. They did not happen in Washington, DC. My parents did everything they could to keep any racial incidents in Washington away from me, and me away from them. Despite their best efforts, however, sometimes it did creep into my life. My most vivid recollection involved St. Cyprian's (a black parish) and Holy Comforter, (a white parish), both Catholic churches I attended during my youth.

One Sunday morning, when I was about five years old, Momma and I were heading to Mass. Services at St. Cyprian's, our parish, began at 12 noon. Holy Comforter's services started at 12:15 p.m. We left the house late, so Momma decided to go to Holy Comforter rather than St. Cyprian's. Besides, Holy Comforter was nearer our home. When we arrived, the only seats available were at the front of the church. So, Momma marched me up front. Just as she knelt down and made the sign of the cross, a white usher came to us and said, "Niggers sit at the back of the church."

I was nervous because I had never experienced anything like that before. Momma, however, knew how to deal with the problem. She slowly made the sign of the cross again, stood up, looked the man in the eye, and whispered "Go to Hell!"

The man was stunned. He said nothing and walked away. I was frightened, not so much by what she said as where she had said it. She pulled me close to her, hugged me, and sat down. At the end of Mass, we went home. Neither Momma nor I ever talked about the matter.

So, when I arrived in England, I knew discrimination existed but I had not seen much of it up close. Although no one ever called me a nigger in

London, other experiences made it clear I was not totally welcome.

For example, in stores it was not uncommon to be treated with utter disdain by shopkeepers and white customers. As a result, I had to be a little pushy to get service. Upon entering a store, I invariably had to ask to be helped. If I was in a queue, I was usually the last person to be served even if I was at the top of the line.

And there were the signs. In the windows of apartments and bed and breakfasts, it was not uncommon to see signs that read "Europeans Only," "No Blacks," or "Coloreds Need Not Apply." While an American accent helped to cushion the discrimination, it did not eliminate it, because people usually saw the color of my skin before they heard my accent.

Stan

Stan Ervin was from Myrtle Beach, South Carolina. Before joining the Army, he studied at Howard University and was involved in the student movement. It was his involvement in that movement that nearly got me in trouble with the Navy.

One Sunday morning, as he and I returned from a party in the West End, we decided to cut through Hyde Park at Park Road and Oxford Street. Just inside the park is Speakers' Corner. Even today, Speakers'

Corner is known as a place where tourists and others go to hear the fringe elements of British society. In the late sixties, most American servicemen did not go there because of the anti-American sentiments surrounding the Vietnam War. That particular Sunday, we decided to check it out.

As we walked along stopping and listening to the various speakers, Stan noticed Stokely Carmichael, a.k.a. Kwame Seku Toure. Kwame was a sixties campus radical well known for his involvement in the Student Nonviolent Coordinating Committee (SNCC). He was very unpopular at home because of his left-wing political leanings. At the time, I was unaware that Stan knew him from Howard University.

As we stood there listening to Kwame harangue the crowd, he suddenly stopped, cupped his hands over his eyes, and shouted, "Ras Man, Stan!"

With that he bounded off his soapbox, waded through the crowd, and hugged Stan. As they stood there laughing and talking, Stan introduced him to me. Just as Kwame and I shook hands, a photographer took our picture. He laughed and remarked, "Poor bastard, got my worst side."

We laughed and thought nothing of it. Stan gave Kwame his numbers, and we continued our journey home.

When I got to the office the next morning, several messages telling me to report to the captain's office were waiting for me. When I entered, I could see the captain was not in a good mood. As I approached his desk, he gestured towards a newspaper he was holding and shouted, "Do you want to explain this shit?"

Squinting to see exactly what he was talking about, I discovered he was holding a morning copy of the London edition of the *New York Times*. Just below his thumb, I spotted the picture of Kwame, Stan, and me.

The more I tried to explain, the more the captain shouted. Finally, he calmed down, listened to my explanation, and accepted the fact that the picture did not accurately depict what was going on. With that, our essentially one-sided conversation ended.

But as I left his office, he shouted after me, "Sailor, you stay the hell out of Speakers' Corner."

I did.

Becky & Kip

Although most of the guys dated frequently, few had steady girlfriends while in London. One exception was Petty Officer Third Class William Kip. His steady was a young woman named Becky.

Kip and Becky were an item around Douglas House and were treated as a novelty for several reasons. First, they were there all the time. They even had a table that was known as semi-reserved for them. Second, Becky was white and Kip made a big deal of it because he preferred not to date women of color, whom he called wire-headed hammers, jungle bunnies, and the like. Third, Kip adored her and believed everyone wanted her because she was white!

One evening, on Kip's birthday, he and Becky came to the club to celebrate. Kip ordered champagne. After fifteen minutes, the champagne had not arrived, so Kip went to check on it. While he was gone, one of the guys asked Becky to dance. Of course, the song was a slow one. Two songs later, Kip returned with two bottles of champagne, one in his hand and the other under his arm. By this time, the other fellow and Becky were really getting into the slow music.

Kip went berserk. He rushed out onto the dance floor and grabbed Becky. The fellow, defending Becky, threw a punch at Kip but missed. Throughout all this, Kip had never put the champagne down. Just then, as the guy was about to take another swing at Kip, the Air Force Police, permanently on duty at Douglas House, rushed into the room and grabbed Kip from behind in a double armlock. As they grabbed him, the champagne turned upside down and poured down Kip's back, causing him, the APs, and Becky, whom Kip was somehow still holding, to slip and slide across the dance floor.

The entire club broke into laughter at the sight of them sliding around on the ballroom floor soaked in champagne.

It was policy to ban people from the club for fighting, but because no one was hurt and it was such a hilarious sight, Kip and Becky were not banned. They *were* restricted in the amount of drinks they could order– three drinks each. Ironically, that was just about the number of drinks in a single bottle of champagne.

✧ CHAPTER TWENTY ✧
The Holidays – Alone!

Three months after arriving in England, I found myself facing Christmas. My homesickness intensified now and I would drift into long reveries of the holidays, home, and memories of childhood. Among my most vivid boyhood memories was attending midnight Mass with my mother. Christmas had always been a very special time.

Everything and everyone was beautiful. I can still see the women parading in their feathered hats, long fox stoles, and other faux-animal coats. The soft, warm colors of their ankle-length coats, covering dresses that ran the gamut of the rainbow, gave me, a young boy, a sense of warmth and safety. The sights and sounds of the season, when blended with the new clothes and perfumes of the congregation at midnight Mass, made for a near-mystical experience.

Just as beautiful and alluring as any of the women was our little church, St Cyprian's. It, too, was decorated in its finest. On the altar were flowers of every color, poinsettias leading the way with their bright red and green. Behind the poinsettias were lighted Christmas trees lining the sanctuary. The church literally shimmered in the brilliance of the silver tinsel and multicolored Christmas lights.

As my mother used to tell me, St. Cyprian's began life in the basement of St. Peter's Roman Catholic Church on Capitol Hill. It was a mission church for blacks who came to work in Washington, DC from the surrounding counties in southern Maryland at the turn of the twentieth century.

Many had been Catholic since the early days of slavery, so they sought a place to worship. The white Catholic churches wanted little to do with them. As a result, they were relegated to the basements or balconies of those churches, like St. Peter's. Many left the church because they weren't allowed to fully participate in the activities in the main sanctuary. They were last to be seated and last to receive communion.

Although there was a church, St. Paul's, built specifically for them, many did not attend it because it was on the other side of the city and not readily accessible due to poor or nonexistent public transportation. As a result, the community that came to make up St. Cyprian's decided to build its own church.

The men purchased St. Cyprian's piecemeal. First they acquired the land on Capitol Hill at 13th and South Carolina Avenue SE. Next, they purchased the granite blocks for the church, the rectory, and the church hall. The actual construction of the church took approximately five years.

Once built, the church was a wonder to behold. Its single spire, which housed the bell, rose more than one hundred feet into the air. Although there were three arched doorways, the center was the main entrance. Over this center doorway towered a beautiful stained glass window; above that was an alcove holding the statue of St. Cyprian. To the left, just inside the church vestibule, stood a life-sized replica of Michelangelo's *Pieta*. Over time the texture of the hands of the statue were worn smooth by the many women who embraced them during times of joy and sadness.

In addition to the midnight Masses, I remembered fondly the May processions, when the white priests would lead the colored children and the rest of the congregation on processions that would start at the church and go down C Street to 12th Street, turn right, then cross three blocks to Lincoln Park, then back down Kentucky Avenue to the church. The police would stop traffic those mornings and allow us colored Catholics to have our processions, which usually stretched two city blocks and took the better part of forty-five minutes to complete.

When we returned to the church after the procession, we prayed. The service consisted of a High Mass with all the bells and smells (incense, smoke, and candles). As a child, I was thoroughly fascinated by it all. To me, Heaven could not be more luxuriant! The mystery of the Mass, the pageantry of the processions, and the sights, colors, and smells of the women and the rituals made for powerful memories.

A keen desire to touch something of those memories led me to church my first Christmas Eve in England. I walked from my little room in the house in Kilburn to the local Catholic church a few blocks away. The night was bitterly cold, and the evening's snowfall had blanketed everything in white. While I was dressed properly, as Momma would have insisted, I shivered nonetheless. As I entered the church, I saw only a handful of people of color present, but that did not really matter.

However, what did matter was that the church was not heated. This, combined with the aloofness of the service, made the church and the streets outside seem even colder and more lifeless. The memories came rushing in once more, and I longed to be home. I wanted to smell the fragrances, hear the sounds, and see the people and surroundings I had known so intimately just a few years before. But none of that was real now. I wanted to call home. I wanted to call Rachel. But instead, I sat in the back of that church and silently wept. I could not believe that I was spending Christmas in such a place. I felt alone and abandoned and oh, so far from home.

The hurt seemed unbearable so I promised myself to never allow those feelings to come over me again. The easiest fix, I reasoned, was to simply stop going to church. So I did. Ironically, in all my letters home to my mother, my aunt, Sister David, (a nun), or anyone else, I never mentioned I had stopped going to church. Emotionally, I had hit rock bottom.

I later learned that while I was having my personal crisis, St. Cyprian's was having difficulties of its own. During her seventy-five years of life, St. Cyprian's was a bastion of black Catholicism on Capitol Hill. Its prime location and the fact that it was less than five blocks from a newer white church, Holy Comforter, made it a target for real estate speculators.

The speculators finally won around 1969. The church was combined with Holy Comforter. Officially, the explanation given was that St. Cyprian's, at seventy-five years, was in such poor condition that it was better to tear it down. Unofficially, the church, the school, the rectory, and the hall fell prey to the land speculators. Word is that when finally sold in the early seventies, the St. Cyprian's package reaped a whopping $700,000 for the Catholic Archdiocese of Washington. Today town homes stand on the site.

✧ CHAPTER TWENTY-ONE ✧
James & Anna

James and I met in 1966 while stationed at the Communications "A" School in Bainbridge, Maryland. He was from Chicago and Jewish. Although neither he nor I had much experience dealing across religious lines, it didn't seem to inhibit our initial friendship. On occasion, before we went to London, he and I would go to the base club and have a bottle of bunny beer. Bunny beer contained only 3.2% alcohol, brewed specifically for the sailors who were under twenty-one. It merely gave us beer breath and made us go to the bathroom. I turned twenty-one in the middle of that summer. Despite my age, I still had to drink bunny beer because most of the other sailors, my classmates, were still under twenty-one.

James and I did not become true friends until we learned we would be stationed together in England. In all honesty, I was hesitant to become friends because he and I competed in class. Both of us considered the

classes boring and our mini-competition helped pass
the time. One week, he would lead the class; the next,
I would lead.

On weekends, James disappeared as often as I did.
So one Friday, I asked him what he did. I was surprised
to learn that, like me, more often than not, he'd go to visit
his girlfriend. When he described Anna, I liked her
because, like Rachel, she seemed to be a decisive and
determined individual. In time, Anna proved to be that
and more.

When James and I arrived in England, we would
joke about how nice it would be if Anna and Rachel
could join us in England permanently. My comments
were based on Rachel's kidding me about coming to
England in the spring. I believe James made his
comments more out of wishful thinking. However,
about two months into our tour, James got the surprise
of his life.

In October 1966, Anna wrote that she was coming to
England. At first we laughed. But it became deadly
serious the day James got the phone call from Anna, who
had just arrived at Heathrow Airport.

Barely eighteen, she had somehow obtained pass-
port, airfare, and booked her flight without her or
James's parents learning about it. Her boldness and
determination were shocking, and her arrival made most

of us jealous. It also gave me the courage to hope Rachel would do the same. Excitedly, I wrote and told her about Anna's arrival without hinting that I hoped she would make the same decision.

Anna and James lived together throughout his tour of duty in London. Despite not having a work permit, she proved to be just as industrious once in London. Anna had three different jobs during her stay in England. For a time, she worked at the Navy Commissary; then at Whitelaw's, a discount department store near the office; and lastly, at Marks and Spencer's, a major department store on Oxford Street. In hindsight, all of these things were unusual because at the time, living with a girlfriend was unheard of. And even the military wives generally did not work outside the home.

Initially, some of us laughed at how Anna must be cramping James's style. We just assumed her presence limited his access to the parties. However, in reality, Anna's presence was a blessing for both of them. Instead of spending his money on Douglas House and its activities, James and she routinely toured the English and Welsh countrysides. They also traveled to Scotland and Ireland. They enjoyed their stay and traveled more than most of us. James and Anna eventually married back in Chicago. To some degree, I still envy them for their courage and conviction.

CHAPTER TWENTY-TWO

Rachel!

I met Rachel Morrissey in the late spring of 1965. Her sister Fran, who worked with me at the CIA, invited me to meet her new husband Bill, stationed with the Air Force Honor Guard at Bolling Air Force Base. At the time, Fran and Bill lived in an apartment on Park Road in northwest Washington, DC convenient to public transportation, movies, and restaurants. Park Road was in an area where I had always hoped to live. When Fran invited me over, I jumped at the chance to see the apartment and ask how much they paid in rent. To my surprise, when I arrived, Fran's younger sister Rachel was there, too.

Rachel lived with her parents in Red Bank, New Jersey, located in Monmouth County on the Navesink River, near the Atlantic Ocean. Named for the soil on its riverbanks, Red Bank has always been a small town known as a commercial and boating center. Even today, its population is less than 15,000. In the mid-sixties, its population was less than 8,000. It is also notable as the home of the great Count Basie.

When I met Rachel she worked in nursing, primarily with the elderly. I remember that she giggled a lot, wore her hair in a flip, and loved to dance. I loved to dance, too. After dinner that first night, the four of us went dancing and had a great time. When I left to go home, even though I had enjoyed myself, I assumed that was it. I must admit that as I was leaving, I felt really lucky because Fran, known to be quite particular, had introduced me to her little sister.

On the night we met, I realized immediately that I really liked being with Rachel. She was different from most of the people I knew in Washington. She enjoyed simple things, like walks in the park, holding hands, and sharing her opinions. She was also confident, ambitious, and assertive, and seemed to know exactly where she was headed.

Rachel was also adventurous. She owned a blue 1964 Chevy Corvair Monza that she drove everywhere. The day we met she had driven down to DC from Jersey. During the times I went to see her in Red Bank, she would pick me up in New York or Asbury Park and drive all over Jersey, showing me the home she had lived in as a child in Nutley, the beaches at

Asbury Park, and the rest of the area around Red Bank. Throughout the summer of 1965 and until I went to England in the fall of 1966, I got to know that little car and its owner extremely well. It was the gradual growth of the relationship that made it so special. This gradual familiarity, and something that Rachel did in October 1965, signaled to me that she was becoming more than just a friend.

On Friday, October 15, 1965, I threw a party to celebrate my enlistment in the Navy. Although the party was more for my friends, I was having a good time, too. But then the beer ran out. As the host, I had to go get more. When I returned from getting more, Cliff, a childhood friend, and my sister Joanne could hardly wait to tell me that someone special was waiting for me.

As I pushed through the crowd into the apartment, I heard my name called. I turned around, and there, smiling, was Rachel. I could not believe my eyes. I really wasn't expecting to see her. She had driven all the way from Red Bank for my party. Others knew she was coming, but had kept it a secret.

Wearing a pink blouse with a flared collar and matching skirt, she was absolutely beautiful. I hugged her gently and kissed her on the cheek. As I did, I felt a rush of excitement at her nearness and her fragrance. I was absolutely tongue-tied. And, like a dummy, I blurted out, "What are you doing here?"

She smiled and said, "Aren't you having a going-away party?"

Stupidly, and with a sheepish grin, I said, "Yes."

Rachel stayed most of the evening. Although we did not have much time to talk, we did dance a couple of times. Then, just as suddenly as she came, she was gone. It was then I began to realize Rachel was someone very special. *I was impressed!*

Previously, I mentioned my trip home for my brother-in-law's funeral in May 1967. On the way back to England, I went to see Rachel. I could not believe how much I had missed her. During that visit, Rachel confirmed she would come to England as she had promised the previous fall. "And," she continued, "I will be arriving in less than a month." I was absolutely thrilled.

When I returned to London, I focused on cleaning up the apartment and choosing places for Rachel to see. I wanted everything to be perfect for her when she came. Although I had used all my leave to go home for Raymond's funeral, I asked for time off from work anyway. Of course, my request was denied.

Finally, the big day arrived. The tour package she purchased provided transportation to her hotel in

Queen's Way just off Bayswater Road in central London. I was at the hotel within minutes of her arrival. Despite her long flight, she was radiant, and I was beside myself. No one had ever gone to such lengths to show me such care or kindness. We explored her room, taking in the tiny breakfast area, laughed at the lift (elevator) that could barely hold four people, and we basked in each other's company. My heart told me that the lady I loved had come to be with me–*permanently!*

Her two weeks flew by. We went to restaurants and movies, took walks in Hyde Park and around Shepherd's Bush Green, danced at Douglas House until we dropped, and toured the city until the pubs closed and public transportation shut down. Everyone wanted to meet the lady who had come from America to see me, and I wanted her to meet them. I felt really special and above all, loved.

The first time I took her to Douglas House, the guys were standing at the top of the stairs gawking and waiting to meet her. Rachel was dressed in a chocolate-brown miniskirt with a matching brown and white pullover. She wore her hair in a ponytail and sported chocolate-brown mid-calf leather boots. It took all of my self-control to keep from smiling incessantly.

We danced nonstop. We did all of the latest dances: the monkey, the fruge, the jerk, the cha-cha, and the twist. We slow-danced! We fast-danced! Several of the guys tried to cut in, but I would not let them. Then one said, "Harry, let the woman relax. She has just flown across the pond and must be tired."

To which I replied, "Oh, you are just jealous. Besides, you don't know what you are missing." We all got a laugh out of that. My heart was overjoyed.

Each day Rachel spent in England, I introduced her to something new. We explored the tube (subway), riding all over London. We tried various restaurants and different things to eat. On the day she first ate fish and chips, I felt so sorry for her. The deep-fried fish was packaged the traditional way, wrapped in brown paper with an outer wrapper of old newspapers. The fish were bathed in malt vinegar, salt, and pepper. The grease from the concoction was so hot, it burned her fingers. I apologized profusely and kissed her hurt fingers. She laughed, called me silly, but didn't pull her fingers away.

After eating the fish and chips, we walked from Marble Arch to Piccadilly Circus, a distance of about a mile and a half. I talked nonstop. We window-shopped along Oxford Street. Rachel laughed at the girls in micro-miniskirts and the guys in their bell-bottom pants with peace symbols and outrageous colors.

On another day, we tried steak and kidney pie at the Barley Mow, a small corner pub near the office, known for American and British foods. The Barley Mow always had a large crowd, a favorite for the downtown shoppers because of its reputation for serving great food. When the pie came, to my surprise, the steak was not in chunks but in one big piece. In a traditional steak and kidney pie, the beef is chopped up. Somehow, the steak missed being diced. I was upset because I wanted everything to be just right for her.

Next we tried shepherd's pie. A traditional shepherd's pie is a mixture of ground beef, onions, tomatoes, and green peppers topped off with mashed potatoes. In that one, while the potato topping was good, it was merely diced chunks of beef with a few veggies thrown in for flavor. Again, I was disappointed but she seemed not to mind. Although she said she found it interesting, I had to finish the meal for her.

One evening, I took her by my flat. Although I had planned to go out to dinner later, she was insistent upon fixing dinner for my roommate Ted and me. To help Rachel, Ted went into our little freezer and took out some steaks, frozen mixed greens, and an apple pie.

Rachel ordered us out of the kitchen. As we went into the living room, she began working her magic. She never asked for help, so we assumed she must have found all of the pots, pans, and spices on her own.

Forty-five minutes later, she came out of the kitchen near tears. I asked her what was wrong.

Hesitantly, she began to explain. "I put the water in the pot before putting in the frozen greens, but I must not have put in enough because the greens are now burned and stuck to the bottom of the pan." She continued, "While waiting for the water to boil, I placed the steaks and the pie in the oven. I knew they shouldn't be on the same shelf, so I put the pie on top and the steaks on the bottom. But I must not have done that right because the pie now smells and tastes like steaks.

"To add insult to injury, when I tried to sprinkle salt on the steaks, the top came off the shaker. So now we have salt beef instead of baked steaks." With that, she flopped on the sofa and began to cry softly, apologizing for ruining the meal.

Although Rachel had ruined what for us would have been two or three days worth of food, Ted and I thought it was funny. Of course, our laughter only made matters worse.

Finally, after convincing her that things were not that bad, the three of us went out to dinner. To help her feel better, we gave in to her insistence that she pay for the meal. During dinner at one of the little Chinese restaurants in Notting Hill Gate, Rachel admitted she had never attempted to fix a full meal before. Ted and I looked at each other and, in unison, said, "No joke!" We all had a good laugh.

To this day, I look upon those two weeks Rachel spent with me in England as one of the happiest times of my life. I had the one person who meant the world to me by my side, in the place that was fast becoming my real home. As the time for her to leave drew nearer, I dreaded the thought of her leaving and told her so.

In the midst of this, I got a surprise letter from my mother. Momma wrote of her displeasure over Rachel's being with me in England. Although the two of them had never met, Momma had heard me speak often of Rachel, but did not know what to make of her. She liked Rachel's showering me with attention, but she found it intriguing that a twenty-two-year-old would drive from Jersey, and even fly to England, just to see me.

While my mother was thrilled that I appeared to be falling in love with her namesake, to Rachel Butler, this Rachel Morrissey was an enigma. She felt the relationship was on too fast a track. To further exacerbate things, she had not found out about Rachel's trip from me. She heard it, instead, from my cousin Shirley who lived in New York and had met Rachel only once in passing.

At the same time I was dating Rachel and before my transfer to London, my brother Francis was also dating a lady named Rachel, Rachel Samuels, also from New Jersey. On those weekends when I would go to see Rachel Morrissey, Francis would see Rachel Samuels. If Rachel Morrissey could not take me all the way to New York, we would meet Francis along the way. As a result, he heard about the proposed trip to England long before anyone else.

It was during one of Francis's weekend visits with my cousin Shirley (after I transferred to London), when he happened to mention that Rachel was coming to England. However, by the time I got Momma's first letter, Shirley had forgotten about Rachel Morrissey and assumed that the Rachel going to England was my mother, so she decided to call to congratulate her. It was that call that precipitated Momma's letter that arrived while Rachel was in England.

Although she did not state it in her letter, I learned later that Momma was worried Rachel and I would elope, or Rachel would come home from England pregnant, or worse yet, we would not come home at all. In my letters I reassured Momma as best I could.

When I later spoke to her, I told her Rachel and I had no plans to elope. I also reassured her that I loved Rachel too much to put her in the predicament of dealing with a pregnancy and no husband. Finally, I promised her no matter what Rachel and I did, we would come home. None of this seemed to assuage her concerns. Perhaps it was because she knew me too well. Truthfully, had Rachel stayed in England, I probably would not have come home for quite a while.

As the time for Rachel to leave drew near, I begged her to stay. But each time, she would smile and sweetly put me off. I tried to reason with her, stating and restating the obvious, "I have a place of my own where we can stay together and as an American and a nurse, you can get a job here! I will take care of you!" Nothing worked.

In a final act of desperation, I took her to meet James and Anna. By this time, James's girlfriend Anna, who was now nineteen, had been in England nearly a year. Her impetuous flight to London from Chicago seemed to secure their relationship. They had what I wanted and hoped for. I wanted Rachel to see that if a nineteen and twenty-year-old could make it in England, surely two twenty-two-year-olds could, too.

Nothing changed her mind. I began to wonder what was happening to the assertive, aggressive, decisive person I loved. I grew frustrated. Finally, the day before she left, Rachel explained to me, "Harry, I love you so much. But you have to understand that I can't do this to my parents. We can get married when you come home. But I just can't stay here now. I don't know what my parents would think."

I did not care what her parents or mine would think. I only knew I wanted her to stay. I felt crushed, hurt, betrayed! I thought to myself, "I've spent my entire first year in England miserable and alone. Here, standing before me, is the one person I love above all others, and she is telling me she can not stay because she does not know what her parents would think." I felt utterly rejected!

The next day at Heathrow Airport, with little hope, I tried one more time to convince her to stay. She smiled, kissed me on the cheek, and said, "Harry, you will be okay. We will get married when you get home."

I replied, "Rachel, I love you more than you will ever know. But I can't promise you anything if you won't stay and marry me."

She kissed me again, hard and full-mouthed, then said, "You will be okay. We can wait until you come home."

As I rode the bus back to town, I sensed our relationship was ending. My heart told me there would be but one Rachel in my life. I cried bitterly.

Although Rachel wrote and tried to reassure me, I could not get over my feelings of hurt and rejection.

Eventually, I just stopped writing.

CHAPTER TWENTY-THREE

On the Mend

Irene

In the days and weeks following Rachel's departure, I stopped going out. Feeling down, I stayed home, not wanting to be bothered by a soul. My stomach ached, my chest felt heavy; at times I felt as if I could not breathe. I could not sleep. Some days I cried; other days, I just felt god-awful. In hindsight, I realize I was feeling sorry for myself. But at the time, it was a feeling I did not understand and could not shake.

Finally, about two months after Rachel left, John's girlfriend Irene, who lived a block away, invited me over. Reluctantly, I went. The last thing I wanted was to be around two people who seemed to be in love.

I had met Irene McNey when I first arrived in England. Like a lot of the non-Brits I knew, she was from Jamaica. She shared a basement flat with another woman named Barbara Codderington. What I remember about Irene was that she had a four-year-old son Peter, she loved to argue, and she always struck me as being a little short-tempered. However, I accepted her as a friend because she allowed me to bring Samuel around to play with Peter. And because of Samuel and Peter, I began to visit on a regular basis. However, any friendship Irene and I had almost ended before it got started.

One afternoon, Samuel and Peter got into an argument that led to a tussling contest. I decided to intercede. When I separated the two boys, Irene yelled at me because she thought I was a bit rough with Peter. When I told her Peter had called me a nigger, she said nothing. I insisted she make Peter apologize. She refused and called me a wall-crawling insect. I grabbed Samuel by the hand and assured her that she would never be bothered with me again. However, that was a hollow threat because while John and I were roommates, I often had to go to her house to collect his share of the bills.

The day Irene invited me over after Rachel left, she told me that she had someone she wanted me to meet. "Besides," she continued, "I have heard some of the nasty comments others have been making about how Rachel jilted you."

I told her I did not give a damn what she or others thought. Ignoring me, she continued, "You need to get out and have some fun and get over Rachel 's leaving. If it is to be, it will be."

As I sat in Irene's living room, a very attractive, impeccably dressed woman came in. Irene introduced us. Her name was Joyce. She worked as a striptease dancer at one of the clubs in downtown London. Joyce was tall, very dark, and had a real flair about her. She had long flowing hair, bright red nails, and the grace and movements of a dancer.

I was not sure what to make of her being there. Initially, I thought Irene was trying to match us up. So I decided to go along with the program. After a few drinks and small talk, I found out Joyce was there because Irene had told her of my aspirations to become a professional singer. At the time, I had been taking vocal lessons for more than four years, both at home and in England. Irene had mentioned the name of my vocal coach, Robert Johnson, to Joyce, who immediately recognized him as one of the best coaches in London.

Joyce asked if I was serious about singing. Indignantly, I answered, "Yes!"

She gave me the name of a man who was looking for a singer. I called and made an appointment to see him. He was the owner of the Phoenix Strip Club on Old Compton Street in Soho. Two weeks later, I went for an audition.

When I arrived at the club, Joyce was there with a few of her friends to give me encouragement and support. What they did not realize was that their support was more of a distraction than help. They were wearing work clothes that consisted of g-strings, pasties, and negligees. I had never seen women work in those kinds of clothes before. The ladies were on break between shows. Immediately after the audition, the manager hired me on the spot, paying me five pounds a night. I could hardly believe my good fortune.

Later, I learned that as the club singer, I had two functions: give the ladies a chance to relax between shows, and give the patrons a chance to go to the bathroom. The dancers and I worked on the same floor-level stage space between the bar and the bathroom. So when I performed, the men invariably walked across the stage to get to the bathroom. But that did not matter to me because I was singing professionally. Unfortunately, within a month, the Navy learned about my singing and ordered me to stop.

I was grateful to Joyce for trying to help me during a very difficult period. Sadly, life wasn't as kind to Joyce as she was to me. Joyce married within a year of our meeting, and while on their honeymoon, she and her new husband Robert, an Air Force veteran, were in a tragic auto accident in the French Alps. Joyce was disfigured but survived. Robert died at the scene. My heart went out to Joyce. How dare death take such a dynamic young man while leaving his widow irreparably harmed? Robert's death caused us all to slow down a bit.

Irene next introduced me to her friend, Sheilah Smythe. Sheilah was in her early thirties, at least ten years older than I. When I met her, she had just come out of an abusive marriage that had lasted nine years. She, too, was born in Jamaica and had grown up in England. Like Joyce, she was statuesque and very beautiful. She was, without a doubt, the most thoroughly British black woman I had ever met. Her demeanor, manner of speaking, and straightforward way of addressing people and issues fascinated me.

The day I met her, she was wearing a deep-red chemise dress with black buttons down the front, low-heeled black shoes, and her hair was in a French twist. Despite being a mature and focused woman, she had a girlish way of provoking me by giggling and calling me "little boy."

She had a deep voice with a full, throaty laugh, which I loved. She was also opinionated, and we enjoyed arguing. I just knew there wasn't a snowball's chance in hell that such a sophisticated lady would find me interesting. About two weeks later, Sheilah insisted that Irene give me her number. I called, not really knowing what to expect. To my surprise, she invited me out. We went to the movies and back to her place for dinner.

Sheilah had a son Chet, who was about eight years old. I had met him because he and Peter, Irene's son, were friends. That evening we did absolutely nothing but sit, talk, and laugh. I felt ten feet tall. She actually liked me!!!

The time I spent with Sheilah is now a total blur. She pampered me and showered me with affection. I learned to eat and like British food. She fixed boiled potatoes and lamb chops. She loved tarts. And there was always plenty of Guinness around. I learned to like that, too. We talked on the phone for what seemed like days. When I wasn't at her flat in Hammersmith, I could hardly wait to get there. Soon I began to pull away from my circle of friends at Douglas House. Sheilah did not mind this because she really did not like Douglas House. As she put it, "There were too many bloody, rowdy Americans!"

It did not take me long to realize I was getting in way over my head. And no sooner had the realization hit me, when she called in a playful mood and said, "Little boy, we have to get a handle on this."

I had no idea what she was talking about. I thought she was joking. However, about two weeks later, she told me in no uncertain terms, "Harold, we have to end this."

I knew she was serious because she rarely called me Harold unless she wanted to make a point.

About a week later, our relationship ended. It was on the same day as the Fall 1967 Anti-Vietnam War demonstrations in London. That October day, I was watching the demonstration from the seventh floor of the office building at North Auldley where I worked.

We weren't too busy, so I called Sheilah just to say hello. She sounded a little sad. She asked what I was doing and I replied, "I am watching all those niggers down there protesting." With that, she said, "I told you never to use that word around me." Then she hung up.

I was dumbfounded. I called back, but she would not answer the phone. I went to her flat, but she would not answer the door. I could not believe such a trivial thing could end what I thought was becoming a very special relationship. After a while, I stopped trying to make amends in the hope that I could manipulate the situation. I hung out at the places I knew she liked, but she never appeared. I even walked around the markets in Hammersmith and Shepherd's Bush, but no Sheilah. She stopped coming by Irene's house. She was obviously avoiding me and the places we used to go. After a while, I just let go.

I did finally talk to Sheilah at length the evening of Irene and John's wedding reception held in a flat on Queensway Road. I walked in and there sat Sheilah by herself. She hugged me and kissed me gently on the cheek and said, "How have you been, little boy?" with that familiar giggle.

I was overjoyed to hear her calling me that again. Although it had been nearly a year since we had last spoken, it was as if nothing had changed. We spent the evening laughing, talking, dancing, and reminiscing about old times. When the evening ended, I walked her to the corner, tried to kiss her, watched her get into a cab, and promised to call. She laughed and said not to. Of course, I did not take her seriously.

A few days later I called. She was very British—polite, but coldly formal. During the call, she reminded me that when we first met, she had insisted that I not take any pictures. She also asked me to tear up her phone number. She explained that, from the beginning, she knew it would have to end this way because, as she put it, it was the only way it could end because of our ages.

"Besides," she said, "we had fun, didn't we, love?"

That's when it sunk in. The entire affair had lasted no more than two months because she had planned it that way. I had been a fun fling for her!

Looking back over the years, I now fully appreciate what Sheilah did. I understand now that while she was an older woman toying with a man-child's emotions, she taught me the value of knowing when to let go and how to walk away with grace and dignity. The weekend before I left London in 1968, I called Sheilah. We talked for a little while, but she would not see me. And when I said goodbye for the last time, she laughed and said, in her very proper British accent "Goodbye, Harold." Then, after a pause, "Go and have a nice life, little boy!" We both laughed and hung up.

Every now and then, I think of her and say a prayer of thanksgiving for her. Over time, the memory of Sheilah Smythe has helped me to put into perspective what I believed was Rachel's rejection. I now understand that Rachel did not reject me. I rejected her because of my boyish impatience and impetuousness.

✧ CHAPTER TWENTY-FOUR ✧
Cheryl

Irene was not the only person to introduce me to someone after Rachel left. Stan Ervin, one of the Bros, a draftee who somehow managed to spend his entire enlistment in London, introduced me to a young lady named Cheryl Miller. According to Stan, Cheryl was someone who, like me, seemed down because she, too, was separated from her fiancé. When I heard that explanation, I became suspicious because guys rarely introduced other guys to girls unless there was a problem.

Cheryl was from New York and attended school in Germany. She and four of her girlfriends had managed to get their hands on that semester's money, and rather than attend classes, they took the opportunity to see Europe. Because they were not the most frugal people, they managed to blow all their money in less than a month while traveling between

Douglas House   197

Frankfurt, Germany, and London. Of course, most of the money had been spent staying in first-class hotels. By the time they arrived in London, they were broke.

At the time, Stan and Kip were part of a five-person roommate group renting a three-bedroom apartment just off Lancaster Gate on Bayswater Road across from Hyde Park. The apartment was fabulous, and they knew it. It was also very expensive. They were paying more than £300 a month (around $700) for the third-floor walk-up. However, they did not mind the cost because the apartment made an ideal place to attract and impress women.

The guys had met Cheryl and her friends at Samantha's, a nightclub in Soho. Samantha's was on one of the side streets off Piccadilly Circus and sat at the bottom of a long flight of stairs. The entire club was underground and had one of the largest dance floors in the city. The centerpiece of the club was its DJ's booth, a canary-yellow Jaguar that hung from the ceiling by chains. This club was also very expensive. As a result, I usually did not go there unless I was really trying to impress someone.

Another reason I did not like going to Samantha's was because it had a reputation for being a place where bisexuals and homosexuals hung out. Also, some of the patrons made it a point to let GIs know they were not welcome. But that is where Stan and the guys met Cheryl and the ladies we termed "the sistas from the World (USA)."

In short order, the guys learned that Cheryl and the others were out of money. So, being gentlemen, they offered them a place to stay. Since their only other option was sleeping on the streets, the ladies accepted and went to stay at the luxury high-rise over-looking Hyde Park. The girls agreed they would not be staying too long; besides, they were expecting money from home. In exchange for the free food and a place to stay, they were to clean the apartment and wash and press the guys' shirts and uniforms. Besides, the guys assured them, with all the males working rotating duty, most of the time they would have the place to themselves and be perfectly safe. At least that was how it started out. Before long, each of the girls had paired up with a guy. All except Cheryl, that is.

From the beginning, Cheryl balked at the arrange-ments. Her first objection was that she did not trust the guys. Besides, she really was in love with her boyfriend at home and looked forward to getting married. Then she refused to participate in the cleanup details. By chance, the guys learned of Cheryl's absolute refusal to help with the work.

Initially, Cheryl's refusal was only verbal. Then, on the days she was to do uniforms, she refused to iron them; instead, she washed them and folded them up. That was not a problem because the guys had not given up on her sexually. But Cheryl would not have anything to do with any of them. As a result of her obstinacy, most nights Cheryl found herself either sitting up all night or sleeping on the floor in the living room, cold and alone. Finally the guys put their heads together and decided if she would not do her chores, they would force her to sleep with one of them.

For the next couple of weeks, the guys made a point to bring home someone who could only be entertained in the living room. This, they reasoned, would force Cheryl to lay down in one of the rooms. Once there, so the plan went, Cheryl would fall prey to someone. That ploy ended after two nights of Cheryl's yelling at the top of her voice, "No, G-d damn it, I said no!" Her shouting was so loud that the guys feared the neighbors might call the bobbies. After that, Cheryl decided to take matters into her own hands, so to speak.

Because the guys worked shifts, it was rare that all of them were home at the same time. Cheryl took advantage of that.

The guys had devised a system of signals and signs to let each other know when they were in a room with a girl. Over the next couple of weeks, Cheryl was able to decipher their code. So, to get a good night's sleep, she would go from room to room, leaving one of the signs at the door. When the shift workers came in and saw the signs they thought only they understood, they would go sleep on the floor or the sofa in the living room. Cheryl kept up her charade for nearly a month.

When she was discovered, the guys were in such a panic that they held a meeting at Douglas House away from the girls. That's when they decided to get rid of Cheryl. Stan suggested Cheryl be given to me as a gift to get me over Rachel. When I heard of Cheryl's antics, I figured I had to meet her and soon discovered I really enjoyed her company. However, when she spoke of her boyfriend, it reminded me too much of my own situation. I saw no point in pursuing the matter. I did get the guys to leave her alone and let her stay, but Cheryl went home soon after that. Every now and then, particularly when I see shoes on display, ties tied in a knot, or socks in a ball (the signals), I smile and wonder what ever happened to Cheryl. I hope she and her guy eventually married and lived happily ever after.

✧ CHAPTER TWENTY-FIVE ✧
Party at Harry's

After a couple of weeks of moping over losing Sheilah, I began to accept that I had played a part in allowing Sheilah to use me. So I decided to do something that usually worked when I felt down; I threw a party.

My flat on Leighton Gardens had always been known as a place for a good party. I invited everyone I knew from Douglas House. All of the guys came and many of them brought girls I had never met. The guys generally liked my parties because I had a reputation for having plenty of food, booze, and more women of color than at most parties.

As previously mentioned, in London, most of the women of color were West Indians, East Indians, or Africans. And when I threw a party, I would convince some of them to cook. As a result, my parties generally had a different flavor and a variety of foods from around the world. Despite this, every now and then, what I called a " dumb Americanism" would pop up.

Some of the black GIs would refer to the non-European women as "wire-headed hammers." This derogatory term was a reference to their not using hair straighteners, excessive oils, or relaxers. This particular day, a GI named John Harrison called one of the African women a "wire-headed hammer" to her face.

The woman did not know the term. Then John decided to enlighten her. The woman was incensed. During the argument that ensued, she cursed John in three different languages, English, French, and Swahili. Then she demanded to know why he thought he should get away with such a dumb-ass remark. John smiled, puffed out his chest, and commented, "Hell, I'm an American and you should be damn proud to have my company!"

John's reply only made matters worse. The woman and her friends threatened to take their food and leave. Finally, we convinced John to leave. If we hadn't, the ladies would have made good on their threat. The choice was easy: keep John, no party; no John, we party. So we physically put John out. And we partied!

CHAPTER TWENTY-SIX

Double Trouble

I recall how the sexual antics of the GIs could be deadly. Fortunately, more often, they were just downright funny. One such incident involved a sailor named Henry, his landlady, her husband, and their daughter.

One evening, Ted Jones and I were at home watching the evening news when the doorbell rang. I went to the door and there was Henry, standing with a suitcase in hand and his pea coat under his arm. He had the most frantic look on his face I have ever seen. I invited him in and asked what was wrong.

"I need a place to stay," he answered.

By this time, Ted had joined me at the door. We both wanted to know why he could not go back to his flat in Cricklewood. He said he had a fight with his landlord and had to leave. We invited him to stay with us, and over the next couple of weeks, the story emerged in small pieces.

It seems everything was going well with Henry and his landlord and landlady until he met their daughter. She was about nineteen years old and quite attractive. For a while Henry would meet the girl away from the house. It appeared as if a romance was beginning to blossom.

Then one afternoon while he was at home alone, Henry heard a knock at the door; when he opened it, there stood the landlady in a skimpy negligee. As she put it, she wanted "a cuppa shugga."

Not knowing what else to do, Henry invited her in. According to him, as he went to get the sugar from the cupboard, the landlady grabbed him. Before long, they were engaged in an amorous embrace. One thing led to another, and the afternoon turned into early evening.

Realizing how late it was, the landlady frantically hurried downstairs to her own flat. However, as she opened her door, who should be standing there crying but her daughter. The daughter insisted they confront Henry. So the two of them sat down with Henry and came to an agreement not to see him again, except on business. This agreement lasted barely a week. Before long, Henry was amicably involved with both the landlady and her daughter, seeing them on alternate days.

Then one day the landlady's husband came home early and found his daughter crying. When he asked her why, she spilled the beans. He was furious.

Henry, home at the time, heard the commotion and had just enough time to place some of his belongings in a suitcase. As the landlady's husband was stomping up the front stairs to get Henry, the landlady was knocking on the back door to make sure he escaped. Although he was able to throw his uniforms in the suitcase, the only civilian clothes he salvaged were the clothes on his back.

Later, we also learned that the landlady's husband was triply upset because, while Henry was having affairs with his wife and daughter, *he* had been trying unsuccessfully to seduce one of Henry's girlfriends.

✧ CHAPTER TWENTY-SEVEN ✧
Home-Front News

Occasionally, we would get news from home via the mail, but most of what we saw came from the British press. The Vietnam War was a distant thing for me. However, it came home to me when Raymond was killed in action. Before Raymond's death, Vietnam and the War were things that took place *over there*. After his death, the Middle East conflict, the protest marches, the assassinations, and the civil unrest at home all seemed to touch me more deeply. In my letters home to my mother, I told her how the British depicted us as being out of control because of the turmoil. I cried the first day I saw a protest march in Washington on television and the Army camped out on the steps of the Capitol. It made me question why I was in England serving my country if things were so screwed up at home.

Douglas House

Then came Dr. King's and Robert Kennedy's assassinations. They evoked the deepest sense of hurt and despair for me as an American. On the day King's assassination hit the papers, I was on the way to work when I ran into my roommate Ted in front of the office building. He and I were standing there talking about the shooting. All of a sudden, a white sailor approached us smiling, shoved a copy of the *Daily Mirror* newspaper in front of us, and said, "Take a look at this. Somebody finally got that SOB!"

Although both of us were too shocked to respond, Ted later told me that after Dr. King's death, he considered going AWOL (absent without leave). "What's the point if they're going to shoot us like dogs and laugh about it?" he asked me bitterly.

The day I learned of Bobby Kennedy's death, I had stopped at Douglas House for a drink. I was supposed to meet Marki, whom I had just started dating, but did not get to her house until late. When I arrived, she was not home, so her roommate, Joan Belton, let me in. As I was sitting there waiting, Joan called me to see a televised news report about what was going on in Los Angeles. I sat in stunned silence, watching as Bobby Kennedy bled to death on the floor of a Los Angeles hotel. Once again, I felt betrayed as an American serviceman overseas. I hung my head, left without saying a word, and went home, just wanting to be alone.

The riots that resulted after Dr. King's death, particularly those in Washington, touched me most deeply of all. Once again, I was at someone's home watching television. I sat in horror as I watched streets I had traveled in my youth being burned. Many of the streets were near my parent's home. I waited and listened for more news, trying to see if my family was safe. I tried to call home, but the trans-Atlantic phone lines were busy. It took the better part of two hours to finally get through. I spoke to my mother. She was concerned because my younger brother Butch had not come home. I asked her to plead with him to stay off the streets. She said she would.

For the next couple of days, I found myself glued to the television, again resenting America and all Americans for embarrassing me by their inability to get along at home. I have never felt so ashamed to be an American as I did during those days.

CHAPTER TWENTY-EIGHT

The London Demonstrations

Earlier I mentioned the Fall 1967 Anti-Vietnam War demonstrations in London. One of the saddest events I personally witnessed in England took place that day.

The day had started slowly. It was rare that we wore our uniforms during my tour of duty in London. However, that day we had been ordered to bring our uniforms to work and we were told to arrive before 7:30 a.m. and enter through the side door of the North Audley Street building. We had been cautioned about the protesters and the potential for danger.

The demonstration got into full swing around 9 a.m. By that time our building was secure. The front door was chained and bolted, the lights were out, and no one could see in. Armed sentries stood inside the doors and out of the light. What we did not know was

that the demonstrators' attention was focused on the
Embassy, located diagonally across from us.

As the demonstrators came down North Audley
Street, we could see from the seventh-floor windows
of our office building that the marchers stretched from
Grovenor Circle and North Audley Street to Baker
Street and North Audley, a distance of approximately
two miles. Demonstrators were not in the middle of
the street, as I had seen them in the States. Instead,
they were shoulder-to-shoulder from the front of the
buildings on one sidewalk to the front of the buildings
on the opposite sidewalk. And that was how they
came up the street, with banners and flags fluttering in
the wind. There were American flags, Soviet flags,
peace flags, Viet Cong flags, and homemade signs and
placards. As they marched, they were chanting over
and over, "No, no, no more war!" and "Hey, hey, ho,
ho, LBJ has got to go!"

As the marchers approached the circle, the British
bobbies channeled them into the park in Grovenor
Circle. There they chanted, danced, and played music
for approximately three hours. Then the bobbies
decided to disperse the crowd, but the crowd would
not leave.

From my vantage point, I saw the bobbies
assemble riders on horseback along the side of the

Embassy behind vans. At a signal, the vans pulled back, and the riders charged into the crowd. The crowd pulled back and then surged forward, engulfing the first rider. The rider and horse were lost in the mob. Then I saw the mob kicking, poking, and stomping something—I could not make out exactly what.

There was a second charge of the mounted officers. They formed a cordon around the fallen police officer and his mount. Somehow, they managed to get both the rider and his mount out of the crowd. But as they did, I noticed the horse appeared to be lame, and both he and his rider were covered in blood.

Later I learned that the rider had sustained a severe beating but would survive. The horse, however, was not as fortunate. While they were lost in the mob, someone had stabbed the horse repeatedly with an umbrella; others had stomped it so severely the horse suffered internal injuries and had to be put down.

This story is significant to me for two reasons: first, before this event, I had never seen an animal as large as a horse nearly beaten to death; second, during the presidential elections of 1992, this demonstration was used to graphically show that candidate Bill Clinton was unworthy of holding the office of the presidency. His detractors alleged that he had led public demonstrations against America while a student overseas.

I was there and saw some of the people who led the demonstration. Bill Clinton might have been there, too. But as a twenty-two-year-old watching the demonstrators, I find it hard to believe that the then-future president was anything more than another twenty-something caught up in a very tumultuous time.

✧ CHAPTER TWENTY-NINE ✧
Marki!

Although I did date, I never had a steady girl-friend while I was in London (other than Rachel), until I met Margaret Bradshaw, or Marki as she preferred. We met about six months after she came to England. Later I learned she had arrived around the same time Rachel left.

Marki had lived in Canada for nearly five years before she decided to come to England to visit her two sisters, Gloria and Maria. When my friend Fitz introduced us, Marki was living with her sister Maria and eight other ladies in a three-story house in East Putney. Fitz wanted me to meet her because he knew I was still dealing with Rachel's rejection. Fitz knew the girls because he had taken a room in the house and assumed the role of big brother, protecting them from what he termed unscrupulous people, particularly military personnel.

Since Marki, Maria, Elaine, and Elaine's sister Joan were from Barbados, most had known each other before coming to England. The others were from Trinidad and St. Lucia. At home all of them had visited each other. So when they found themselves far away from home in England, they renewed their friendships.

When Fitz initially suggested I meet Marki, I was not interested. Finally, after two or three calls, I promised him I would stop by. That evening, a Monday, I went by rather late and did not expect to see anyone. To my surprise, Fitz and the others were in the living room watching TV.

When I walked in, I assumed Marki was one of the girls watching TV with them. But then, this other young lady walked through the room on the way to the kitchen. She did not speak and, unlike the others, she did not seem interested in talking or watching television. At first I thought she was just plain snooty, but they told me she was preparing for work the next morning. So I decided I would badger her if she came through the room again. On her second trip through, I made a snide remark about people entering rooms and not speaking. To my surprise, she spoke, apologized, and then began talking to me.

Marki was wearing a light-colored sweater and a dark miniskirt. Her hair, which she wore combed back, reached the middle of her back. After a few pleasantries, I did not know what else to say, so I asked one question that usually seemed to get a girl's attention.

"Did you know my roommate and I are having a party Friday?"

"No," came the reply. "Can we come?" It worked like a charm. There was only one problem. It was the Monday between paydays, and I had no money. Also, I had not planned a party. On the way home that night, Ted berated me for promising to have a party just to get to know Marki.

Luck was on my side. For two nights straight, I played the slots at Douglas House and on the second night, I hit not one, but two, jackpots for $35 each. The party was on.

Friday night came and the party started at 9:30. We had a house full of guys, but few ladies. Then around 10:30, in came Marki and the rest of the women from East Putney.

As soon as I could, I cornered Marki and began talking to her. However, because it was my party, it was my responsibility to ensure there was plenty of food, booze, and munchies. It was also my responsibility to make sure the military personnel were on their best behavior. It was bad enough that we had Air Force guys partying with sailors. But to add to the mix, we had Royal Marines and Royal Air Force personnel, too, and both were noted for starting fights for the fun of it.

As I attended to the international military contingent, I noticed that one of the Air Force guys, Doug Holmes, had danced with Marki twice. Doug was from Washington, DC, and had taken Marki out once or twice before I met her. To preclude his taking further advantage of my being busy and to forestall any other activities on his part, I devised a plan.

My plan was to get Marki to help with the party. So I asked her if she would help me with some of the coats. To my surprise, she said, "Yes." Immediately, I took her to the room where the coats were and asked her to watch them while I collected other coats. She agreed. So, for the rest of the evening she watched coats and allowed me to bring her food and drinks. We had a really fun time getting to know each other in the middle of a party without interference *from* the party. Before the evening ended, I asked her out.

On our first date, I met Marki at Notting Hill Gate tube station, a transfer point on the blue line, which ran from her office at a bank on Thread Needle Street in central London. We went to see "The Many Faces of Eve" at the Notting Hill Odeon. Afterwards we stopped at a Blimpies and had a sandwich. Marki caught the last train to East Putney, and I waited nearly an hour for the last bus to Kensal Rise. Although it was cold, I did not mind the temperature as I relived our date.

Before long, Marki and I were seeing each other regularly. During a date, she mentioned her desire to go to Denmark. At the time, I belonged to a travel club, so I mentioned to the club manager that I was looking for tickets to Denmark. He checked and within days called to say he had nothing going to Denmark, but did have bargain tickets for a seven-day trip to Lourdes in the South of France. The tickets were cheap ($70 each) because they entailed escorting school children. I chuckled because I knew Marki would not want to go to Lourdes.

Lourdes is a small village in the Pyrenees Mountains in southern France. During the latter part of the eighteenth century, Mary, the mother of Jesus, is reported to have appeared to three children there. During the apparitions, people reported being cured of many illnesses. Since then, Lourdes has become known for both its physical and spiritual healings. Before this, I had never thought of visiting Lourdes. Besides, it was a place for the sick and the dying. At

twenty-two, the last thing on my mind was being sick
or dying. Despite my misgivings about the trip, I
mentioned it to Marki. To my surprise, she thought
the trip was a wonderful idea. So there I was, stuck
going on a trip I did not want to take.

We left for Lourdes on a Wednesday. Escorting
and watching the children was all we had to do.
Basically, we made sure none of them got off the train
before arriving in Lourdes. Others were responsible
for keeping them in check and safe.

We met the kids at Victoria Station and boarded
the train with them for the English Channel. Once the
train got to the Channel, we changed to the Ferry and
met other school children for the crossing. When we
landed at Calais in France, it was our responsibility to
ensure that all the children caught the train to
Lourdes. And that was the extent of our escort duties.

When we arrived in Lourdes early the next
morning, buses were waiting to take us to our hotel,
the Pan-A-Rama. The tour company had booked us in
separate rooms next door to each other. The rooms
were neat, clean, and comfortable. But the hotel had
what to us were a few unique amenities, like a
communal bathroom and showers at the opposite end
of the hall.

The most unique thing was an object in both rooms: a bidet. Neither one of us had ever seen one before. At first we thought it was for washing feet. Then we thought it might be for keeping ice. But there was an ice bucket in each of the rooms.

Finally, I got up the courage to ask one of the young ladies in housekeeping. She blushed, giggled, then turned and walked away in a hurry. I was baffled. Soon after, one of the more matronly housekeepers knocked at my door and explained to me in perfect English how to use the bidet. I was so embarrassed. It took me awhile to tell Marki how I learned about the bidet. Even now, I cannot believe how naïve I was.

When Marki and I went to Lourdes, I had expected the trip to be a romantic getaway. That notion died as soon as we got there. After exploring each other's rooms, we decided to meet in the dining room for the noon meal. When I came down, Marki had already made friends with a young French couple around our age. The young lady spoke some English and was rather attractive. Her friend, a young man, seemed strikingly handsome.

However, as I reached the table and sat down, I was startled when he turned to face me. He had a terribly disfiguring facial cancer that covered the other side of his face. I smiled and spoke awkwardly, but it was too late. I had visibly reacted to his appearance. Although we continued to talk, I could barely eat. After informing us that they had come to Lourdes seeking a miracle, they graciously excused themselves and returned to their room. I felt very stupid. Marki laughed at my embarrassment, which made me feel even dumber!

While in Lourdes, we took several side trips. One of the more humorous ones was a donkey ride up a winding mountain path to an old windmill over-looking the city. We thought the donkey ride would be a lot of fun. It turned out, however, to be a disaster.

Before deciding to go on the donkey ride, I noted that I had seen donkey carts along the trail. As a result, several of the women decided not to wear pants. When we got to the starting point for the ride, all of the carts were out. So, if you wanted to ride, you had to sit in a saddle. And, to make matters worst, the saddles were Spanish saddles. Those particular saddles have horns, and horns make riding sidesaddle nearly impossible.

But Marki was determined to ride this donkey. As she struggled to climb on, she realized there was no graceful way to mount the critter. And just as she finally positioned herself on the beast, it urinated.

Of course, the urine splashed off every nearby rock, soaking me and one other person standing nearby. Luckily, Marki stayed clear. Oh, how she laughed at the sight and smell of me in donkey urine! Just as the animal finished, it took off on its own, much to Marki's frustration. Nothing we tried could halt the beast.

Finally, one of the tour guides managed to slow the animal down. Marki jumped off and refused to get back on, so we had to walk our donkeys the rest of the tour. Needless to say, by the time we got back to the buses, everyone knew what had happened to us. As the day grew warmer, I began to smell rather foul. Marki began calling me "donkey boy." Fortunately, neither the name nor the smell stuck permanently.

Marki really got into the spirit of Lourdes. She wanted to go to all of the prayer sessions, say the rosaries, walk the Stations of the Cross, go to the Grotto, and attend the Masses. The more she *got into* Lourdes, the more I began to think our trip was a real waste of my money.

One day while sitting in the outside café drinking a beer, I met a priest from Boston who escorted groups of Americans to Lourdes annually. He confided that the trips were a way for him to help his parishioners in their spiritual growth, see France, and get away. Over the years he had made more than ten trips. As he put it, "I have seen everything there is to see in Lourdes."

So he offered to show me a little of Lourdes that tourists don't often see. He introduced me to some of the best restaurants and bars in the little town. He was just what I needed. God had sent me a beer-drinking priest to keep me company, while Marki went to the Grotto. Slowly though, the little expressions of faith I encountered began to introduce me to what I knew Lourdes was really about. These expressions weren't earthshaking events, just little catalysts that kept pushing and prodding me.

The first of these occurred on the third day of the trip. I had reluctantly agreed to go with Marki down to the Grotto. As we stood in the crowd, a priest was explaining exactly where the water from the Grotto had originally sprung from the ground. Mid-sentence, he stopped, looked out over the crowd, pointed to me, and asked me to raise my hand. Then, he asked me to look down at my feet.

"There," he remarked, "just below that gent's feet is a gold plate marking the exact spot where the water originally came up out of the ground."

Sure enough, I was standing on a gold plate. That was unreal. Sheepishly, I moved.

The next event took place a day or so later. We were collecting water to ship home. At one of the many fountains, a woman, who to me typified a peasant, offered me a drink from a communal cup. I found her appearance and demeanor repugnant. She was dirty, her head was wrapped in a threadbare scarf, and she smelled terrible. I took one look at her and decided there was no way I would drink out of a cup after her. She insisted. Then Marki insisted. Others around me began insisting, too.

Rather than create a scene, I took the cup and drank from it. Although I had drunk from the fountain before, the cup of water she offered seemed sweeter than the rest. Ashamed of my behavior, I thanked the lady, turned, and moved on, leaving Marki at the fountain. As I looked back at Marki, she smiled at me. I think she understood

The last of the events occurred the night of the closing services. It had rained most of the day. By evening, the rain had become icy. The priest I met earlier agreed to have a farewell beer with me. I mentioned this to Marki and promised to meet her at the Grotto.

After the beer, I left the hotel bar to go down to the Grotto. I came across another American who had been traveling with the priest from Boston. He, too, had been in the bar and was now trying to make it down to the Grotto in time for the closing prayers. The walkway descending to the Grotto was made of cobblestones and opened onto the plaza just below the steps to the shrine.

While I was walking, he was negotiating the walkway in a wheelchair. One slip of his hands on the chair's wheels and he might have ended up God only knows where, so I helped him down to the Grotto. He thanked me and offered to pray for me. I said nothing and went to find Marki.

I felt ashamed that I had gone to Lourdes for the wrong reasons. It was only after I returned to London that I began to realize the significance of Lourdes, those events, and Marki.

When I wrote my mother to tell her about the trip to Lourdes, she was pleased. For the longest time, my mother had dreamed of me becoming a priest, so my going to Lourdes gave her a glimmer of hope that I might still do that.

Instead, the week in Lourdes had begun to cement my relationship with Marki.

But about two months after our Lourdes trip, Marki left England for Canada.

During the time Marki was preparing to leave, many of the guys began to either propose to their girlfriends or actually get married. Among the first couples to get married were Marki's sister Maria and her boyfriend, Ricky Barnes. Next were Ted Jones and Barbara Codderington. Then John Williams and Irene McNey.

At the time, I was still in a bit of a quandary over Rachel. I knew I still cared, but I could not get over my feelings of rejection. Besides, by that time, the letters from Rachel had dropped off dramatically, further convincing me of the matter's futility. As time grew near for Marki to depart, I began to realize that I loved her as much, if not more, than Rachel. I began to talk to her about getting married. Although she liked the idea, like Rachel, she did not want to get married in England. Nothing I said could convince her either.

The Bigot and the Colored Boy—a Lesson Learned

To get married, I needed approval from the Navy because of my work with Naval Security Group. Marki knew this. To convince her of my sincerity, I suggested we apply for permission. Navy regulations stated that U.S. military personnel working in intelligence could marry only other Americans or people from one of the following countries: England, France, Germany, Italy, or Spain. After reading the regulations, I did not expect them to approve my application. I knew others had applied and had not been granted permission, but I suggested we apply anyway.

Getting permission entailed a background investigation of the prospective spouse and her family. Marrying without the check would have been tantamount to committing career suicide. A background investigation could take six months or longer, and there was no guarantee that approval would be given. For example, the following story is about a couple who applied around the time we did, but their application was not approved.

David and Myrna met in England. Like me, David worked in intelligence and had special clearances. Myrna was a student nurse working at the Hammersmith Hospital. Like Marki, Myrna was from Barbados. The couple seemed perfectly suited for each other and did everything together. It was no surprise when David proposed. The Navy refused to approve their request to get married, and the couple never received an official written explanation for the denial. We later learned why.

In researching Myrna's family history, the military discovered that she was essentially a non-person. Sometime between 1943 and 1947, Myrna was born in Venezuela, not Barbados. At the time of her birth, her parents, both doctors, were very active in politics. Within a year of her birth, there was a bloody struggle for power with her parents' political party losing.

Within months of the upheaval, her parents and all of her relatives living in Venezuela were arrested and jailed. Myrna was overlooked during the arrests because she was in the hospital suffering from a bad cold. Within days of the arrests, all of her immediate family were executed. Fortunately for Myrna other relatives in Barbados had heard about the events in Venezuela and managed to sneak into the country to smuggle her out of the hospital. According to the story, for nearly a week they were traveling and hiding with the new baby. Finally, they stowed away on a fishing boat that brought them to Barbados.

When the Navy conducted its checks, they first went to the Barbados government, which then referred them to Venezuela for assistance. What it discovered was that there were no records of Myrna's existence before prep-two (first grade). Barbados had no birth certificate, adoption records, or other documentation to prove who Myrna actually was. Legally, she did not exist before age seven. When the U.S. Navy revealed this single fact to Myrna, she immediately went to the people she knew as her parents and got the entire story.

According to her parents, who were actually her cousins, after the power struggle Myrna's real family had been executed and their bodies destroyed. Once the bodies were disposed of, the ruling party systematically removed all references to them from church and government records. The home in the town where Myrna had been born was leveled. In subsequent years, I am told, Myrna journeyed back to that town. But today, no one there knows anything about the little girl or her family who ceased to exist in the mid-forties.

The news of the circumstances surrounding her birth and the Navy's refusal to give them permission to marry destroyed David and Myrna's relationship.

Despite David and Myrna's difficulties, Marki and I decided to apply anyway. At the time, I worked for Senior Chief Petty Officer Thomas Shelton from Alabama. When we met, I did not like him because he struck me as being a typical good ole boy. He loved telling obscene and/or racist jokes. If he wasn't telling jokes about black people, he was telling them about Wops, Polacks, or Chinks.

When he learned Marki and I were considering marriage, he asked if he could meet her. I said no, but he ordered me to set up the meeting. About a week later, we met at my house.

Senior Chief Shelton arrived with a briefcase full of Navy directives. We sat in the living room and talked for the better part of an hour. He questioned Marki extensively about Barbados. He wanted to know when it became independent, where she had lived since leaving home at eighteen, etc.

When he finished, he told us he thought he could get us permission. His strategy was quite simple. Instead of asking for permission, he reasoned he would ask for a waiver of the regulation. To him, to ask for permission was to concede the point that she did not fit into any of the nationalities mentioned. To seek a waiver meant she did. According to him, Marki was a British citizen who happened to have been born in Barbados.

He submitted the paperwork. To our surprise, less than a month later, we got the Navy's approval to marry.

When the senior chief brought me the news, he made it a point to pull me aside. He said, "Harry, I bent over backwards to get you permission to marry that little girl for two reasons. First of all, I think you are a helluva sailor who deserves the right to marry anyone you want. Second, I wanted to teach you a lesson I hope you will keep with you for the rest of your life.

"You must be more trusting of people, even people you think are bigots. Your distrustful attitude might have cost you your relationship. And besides," he concluded, "every good ole boy ain't necessarily a bigot."

Thirty-seven years later, I am still grappling with that lesson.

✧ CHAPTER THIRTY ✧
Homeward Bound

Marki left England in early July 1968. Again, I found myself alone, and I hated it even more this time. I imagined her rejecting me, too. I was hoping that her tentative agreement to marry me, and the Navy's permission for us to marry, would be enough to keep me focused. It wasn't. I began to back away from Douglas House, particularly on the weekends. To counter this and keep myself from descending into the same kind of rut I found myself in after Rachel left, I began visiting Marki's older sister Gloria.

Gloria was the second person I met from Marki's immediate family. I liked her right away because of her relaxed manner and gentle way of speaking. Marki's younger sister Maria and I had gotten along, but Gloria became a real friend. In many ways, she reminded me of my older brother Francis. She was patient, supportive, and always attentive when I visited or called.

On a few weekends before Marki left England, we would go to Gloria's house in Basildon, near South End on the Sea. Gloria's family would roll out the red carpet for us. There was always a grand time to be had with Gloria, her husband Claude, their sons Colin and Russell, and her younger brother Francis, whom Gloria was raising.

Usually, we would make a weekend of it, arriving early on Saturday morning, laden with bags and boxes filled with American beer, steaks, hamburgers, hot dogs, chips, pretzels, and sodas. We came prepared for a weekend-long picnic. After a while, others in the little town of Basildon began looking forward to seeing the Yanks arrive, too.

One friend of Claude, a gent who called himself the Brewmeister General, became a part of the crowd, too. According to him, he wanted to learn the secrets of American beers. In reality, he simply wanted to savor their flavors and drink as many as he could. Since many American beers were still considered a novelty to most Brits at that time, we were happy to have him learn those secrets. And to help him broaden his learning experiences, we always carried plenty of

Colt 45 malt liquor and Budweiser, Carlings, and Miller beers.

Between the beer and the cookouts, I began to feel at home. That is why, after Marki and the others left for Canada and America, Gloria's house became a partial refuge from my boredom and loneliness during my last three months in England.

When my last week in England rolled around, Wilson McCrae, an Air Force friend, threw a surprise party for me. Reluctantly I went, but the party made me feel even sadder. Wilson sensed this, so he and some friends, including some ladies from Bermuda, decided to help make my last week memorable and fun. While nothing beyond partying took place, they took very good care of me. One young lady, Kat Sherron, took all my uniforms and other dirty clothes and had them washed and pressed.

When she returned them, she smiled and mockingly said, "That, sir, is my gift to ensure that you at least start your new life with clean clothes.

"Somewhere," she continued, "I read it is bad luck to carry dirty clothes across the Atlantic." We laughed.

They cooked all my meals for me and made sure I got one last official look at all the sights in London.

They dropped me at the station Saturday morning, where I took the train to Gloria's, as promised, for one last visit.

That evening, as I sat in Gloria's living room watching television, she came in and asked what was wrong. I dumped the entire story of Rachel and Marki on her. I told her that I dreaded going home because I knew I had made promises to both of them. And although I felt strongest about my more recent promises to Marki, my heart was also being tugged toward Rachel. However, I continued, I could not bear the thought of being rejected again. It was then that Gloria did and said something that has forever endeared her to me.

She sat on the edge of the chair, took me by the hand, and said, "Harry, you are a very good person. From what I can tell, Rachel did not reject you. And I do not see either one of them rejecting you now. You have a very difficult decision to make. I can't tell you what to do. Nor can I tell you what your life will be like with either Marki or Rachel.

"But I can say to you," she continued, "with either choice, you appear to have excellent prospects of a happy future. But please know that no matter whom you marry, you will always be welcome in our home. My boys, my husband, and I think you are a very fine person."

Then she left me to my thoughts and my decision. I left for the trip back to London early the next morning. Wilson, Kat, and the others were waiting at the station again to give me one last send-off before I caught my flight home to the States. The last time I saw all of them, they were standing on the steps of Douglas House waving goodbye and blowing kisses. I managed to smile, although my heart was very sad.

I was departing England feeling just as I had when I arrived—terribly depressed! I did not want to go home.

Home

I arrived back in the USA at McGuire Air Force Base early the next morning. Although I was less than an hour from Rachel and really wanted to see her and talk to her, I decided not to call. Instead, I took a bus to the airport in Philadelphia, and after an overnight stay in the terminal (I missed my connection), I caught the first plane to Washington, DC. My parents were expecting me and were thrilled to have me home, safe and sound. What they did not know, but would soon learn, was that I was immensely unhappy.

For the next month, I refused to contact either Marki or Rachel. I was afraid of being rejected by either or both. I reported to my new duty station, intent on working my way through my sadness.

By the time I reported to the Naval Security Group Headquarters on Nebraska Avenue, in Washington, DC, James and Anna Turner had gotten married and had also transferred to Washington. In addition, John, Ted, and Henry had each married and transferred either to Washington, DC, or Norfolk, Virginia. Fitz, who had introduced me to Marki, had met Rhadda, who was from Burma, and was planning his wedding, too.

So all the couples from London were reassembling here at home. But I was alone, heartbroken, afraid, and indecisive. I wanted so much to talk to my parents about my dilemma, but I could not find the words. Soon my mother began to talk to me about my moodiness. I told her a little about Marki, and she knew about Rachel. But the best she could offer was her support for my decision, no matter what that might be.

One evening, while I was sitting on my parents' porch having a beer with my father, Marki called from Canada. Although she wasn't irate, she was quite determined. She asked if I was planning to come up anytime soon. I hesitantly told her I was not sure. She responded, "You have been home over a month, and I

want to know what you are planning to do. I will not
sit here waiting for you forever."

Within a week, I headed to Canada. By the end of
the following week, Marki and I married. Her assertive-
ness had jarred me out of my lethargy. Two months
later, Marki came to Washington to meet my family.

Epilogue

There is no question that those years in London had a deep impact on me. Now, thirty-seven years later, I have grown to accept London as the place where I stopped being a boy. Those years laid the foundation for my becoming what I believe I am: a man of principle and honor.

Unfortunately, while London provided me with those formative experiences and forged my personal and spiritual growth, it was also a place of immense sadness and pain. Sadness because it was the place where, due to my own selfish and boyish lack of courage, I could not face life and be patient when love was first offered to me. Pain because, in retrospect, I realize I was not as mature as I had believed.

Any growth I have had since London stems from the patience and love of dear Marki, and also because my God has been very tolerant, offering me a second chance to learn what it means to love and to be loved. I am eternally grateful to Him for my time in London.

Marki and I are about to celebrate our thirty-sixth anniversary. James and Anna recently celebrated their thirty-seventh, while Fitz and Rhadda just celebrated their thirty-fifth. Maria and Ricky are divorced, as are John and Irene. Stan eventually married someone he met back here in the States. Ted Jones passed away suddenly sixteen years ago. The others belong to God and time.

And what of Rachel, my dear Rachel? In 1971, I finally got the courage to face her. Although we never really discussed what happened after she left England, she was as beautiful and accepting of me as ever. She later married, but I understand that her marriage did not last. She and her son now live in Georgia. From time to time, I call her because she will always be a very special part of me.

Douglas House? Like some of us, it, too, has become prosperous with age. It is now the Gresham Hyde Park, a four-star hotel. But some things never change. It still has one of the best atmospheres and serves some of the finest cuisine to be found anywhere!!!

And London? That day in late Summer 1968 when I boarded the bus for my flight home, I never expected to see my "hometown" again. Little did I know. Since then, I have been back to or through London at least a dozen times. Like any familiar, much-loved place, the mere mention of its name conjures up the magic of places and people, dear people, of long ago. And whenever I go "home," a little of that excitement always greets me. London–Marki, Rachel, Fitz, Ted, Stan, John, Irene, Sheilah, and all of the others–are still there waiting! They are intricately woven into my being.

I pray this memoir gives them an idea of how much each and every one of them has contributed to who I've become and of my immense satisfaction of having experienced London with them. I loved them all then and I love and thank God for them now, because if any one of them were missing, my life would be incomplete!

Love and Peace!

About the Author

Gerald A. Collins is a native Washingtonian, who attended both public and parochial schools in DC. From 1965 to 1969, and again from 1974 to 1988, he served in the United States Navy aboard ships and at posts both in the United States and overseas as both an officer and an enlisted man. *Douglas House* is his first full-length novel and is based in part on his experiences in London during the sixties.

Printed in the United States
16712LVS00003B/58-306